Throw a six to start then move round the board. If you land on a star square follow the instructions for that number. The winner is the first person to reach the end — you are a star! But beware, if you land on the second last square first, you've failed. Land on No. 95 and you could take a shortcut to the stars.

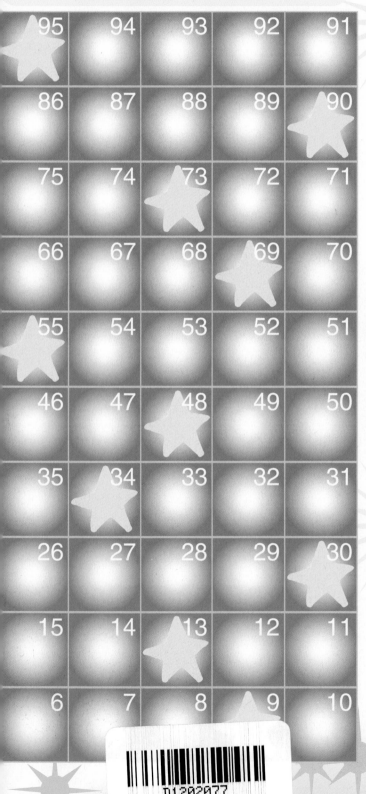

95	94	93	92	91
86	87	88	89	90
75	74	73	72	71
66	67	68	69	70
55	54	53	52	51
46	47	48	49	50
35	34	33	32	31
26	27	28	29	30
15	14	13	12	11
6	7	8	9	10

48. STEPS are on the phone again — this time H wants a date. Go forward 4 spaces.

55. ALL SAINTS are snapped leaving a film premier and you manage to get into the background. Your face is in the newspapers nationwide. Have another turn.

65. You have your hair bleached to look like Christina Aguilera's. Sadly, it all goes horribly wrong. You now have green hair with bald bits. Move back 5 spaces.

69. You see a small child drop a toy in the park. When you run over to hand it back, you realise the dad is mega–star Tom Cruise! Miss a turn while you stare at him for ages.

73. Your dad gives you a lift to a BSB concert, but disaster — the car breaks down. Then a limo pulls up to help. Guess who's in the car? Yup, BSB take you and Pops to the concert in style. Go on 4 spaces.

78. STEPS have split. Why? Cos H and Lee have been fighting over you! Take the blame! Go back 3 spaces.

82. You make a new mate on holiday. She says her brother's in a band — WESTLIFE. Yippee! Have another throw.

90. Your class is appearing on Richard and Judy. Unfortunately, you trip over a camera cable as you enter the set. You fall over in front of millions. Go back 5 spaces.

95. Throw a 2, 4 or 6 and you can move forward 5. Hurray! Throw a 1, 3 or 5 and you can move forward 4. Boo!

D1202077

£5.99

What's in?

Funky Hair! p18

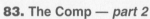
Party Girls! p64

Chocolate! p92

Aww! Cute! p121

Printed and published in Great Britain by D. C. THOMSON & CO., LTD., 185 Fleet Street, London EC4A 2HS. © D. C. THOMSON & CO., LTD., 2000.
While every reasonable care will be taken, neither D. C. Thomson & Co., Ltd., nor its agents accept liability for loss or damage to colour transparencies or any other material submitted to this publication.
ISBN 085116 7292

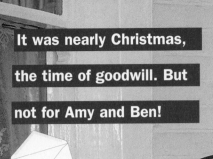

It was nearly Christmas, the time of goodwill. But not for Amy and Ben!

...AND I NEVER WANT TO SEE YOU AGAIN!

SUITS ME — I DON'T WANT TO SEE YOU EITHER!

On The Cards!

WAS THAT YOU AND BEN I HEARD ARGUING, AMY?

SURE WAS. BUT WE WON'T DISTURB YOU AGAIN, MUM — WE'RE FINISHED!

I DON'T KNOW WHAT I EVER SAW IN THE CREEP!

But, a few days later —

I WISH BEN AND I HADN'T FALLEN OUT — I REALLY MISS HIM.

CAN WE LOOK IN HERE? I NEED MORE CHRISTMAS CARDS.

SURE. I WANT A SPECIAL ONE MYSELF, FOR DAMIAN.

5

7

On Christmas Eve —

HERE'S THE MAIL — WE WON'T BE GETTING ANY MORE DELIVERIES BEFORE CHRISTMAS NOW.

I CAN SEE FROM HERE THERE'S NOTHING FROM BEN.

BET HE'S SENT *JEMMA* ONE, THOUGH! I'M GLAD I DIDN'T POST MINE TO HIM — I WOULD'VE LOOKED DEAD SILLY.

COME ON, CHEER UP, IT'S CHRISTMAS!

Amy tried her best to have a good time.

LOVELY! THANKS!

Then it was New Year's Eve.

A NEW YEAR TOMORROW.

I KNOW, MUM.

NEW YEAR — AND A NEW START. HOPEFULLY I'LL MEET TERRIFIC NEW BOYFRIE AND EVERYTHING!

8

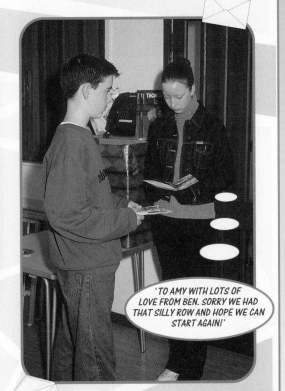

THE END

The Comp

PART 1

ONE Monday morning, at Redvale Comp—

HEY! WHO'S THAT IN THE SPORTS CAR?

IT'S A BEAUT!

YEAH, WHAT A MOTOR!

MM, THE DRIVER'S NOT BAD EITHER, ROZ!

HUNK ALERT!

HI, THE NAME'S GREG. COULD YOU POINT ME TO THE SIXTH FORM ROOM?

SURE, THROUGH THE MAIN DOORS, UP TWO FLIGHTS AND IT'S STRAIGHT AHEAD.

THANKS, CATCH YOU LATER.

THAT GUY IS *SOOO* CUTE!

WHEN I'M 17, *THAT'S* THE KIND OF WHEELS I'M GONNA GET, FREDDY MATE!

ME TOO, HODGE!

DREAM ON! YOU TWO'LL BE LUCKY TO AFFORD BIKES! GREG MUST HAVE LOADSA DOSH!

LUSH *AND* LOADED. A DREAM ON LEGS!

YOU CAN DREAM ON TOO, HAYLEY. SIXTH FORMERS DON'T LOOK AT YEAR NINES LIKE US!

THINK YOURSELF LUCKY, BECKY. HE'S JUST MOVED IN UP OUR WAY AND ALREADY I CAN TELL YOU HE'S TROUBLE.

HOW DO YOU KNOW THAT, AMY?

HE DRIVES LIKE A MANIAC. MY DAD'S GIVEN HIM TWO SPEEDING TICKETS ALREADY. *AND* HE DATES A DIFFERENT GIRL EACH WEEK!

HE SURE IS CUTE, THOUGH.

At break —

HELLO, AGAIN. YOU'RE AMERICAN — I JUST LOVE YOUR ACCENT. WHAT PART OF THE STATES ARE YOU FROM?

CALIFORNIA. MY MOM AND SISTER STILL LIVE THERE.

LUCKY ROZ! THE GUYS ALWAYS FANCY HER!

GUESS WHAT? I HAVE A DATE TONIGHT!

CAREFUL, ROZ — REMEMBER WHAT AMY SAID.

ISN'T HE KINDA OLD FOR YOU?

NO WAY! MIND YOU, MY DAD SURE WON'T LIKE ME DATING A GUY WITH A FAST CAR, SO CAN I SAY I'M ROUND AT YOUR HOUSE TONIGHT, HAYLEY?

UH — I S'POSE SO . . .

THANKS. YOU'RE A PAL!

And, for the next few days —

LAURA, GREG'S TAKING ME TO THAT NEW THEME PARK TODAY.

SHE'S TOLD HER OLD MAN THAT SHE'S GOING WITH YOU, OKAY?

ER — OKAY.

Later —

THERE'S ROZ'S DAD AND STEPMUM! THEY MUSTN'T SEE ME — I'M SUPPOSED TO BE AT THE THEME PARK WITH ROZ!

PHEW! THEY'VE GONE! BUT IT'S NOT FAIR OF ROZ TO PUT US THROUGH THIS.

15

And, the following week —

ROZ? ER — YES — SHE'S HERE, MR CUMMINGS, BUT — SHE'S GONE OUT WITH HAYLEY, I — ER — DON'T KNOW HOW LONG THEY'LL BE.

Next day, Becky told Laura —

I HATED LYING, LAURA. ROZ DIDN'T EVEN WARN US SHE WAS GOING TO TELL HER DAD SHE WAS SUPPOSED TO BE AT OUR PLACE.

I KNOW, BECKY, IT'S NOT FAIR. WE'RE GOING TO HAVE TO SAY SOMETHING ABOUT IT.

THERE'S CLAIRE. THANKS FOR THE INVITE TO YOUR PARTY NEXT SATURDAY — WE'RE ALL COMING!

SHE ISN'T LOOKING AT YOU, LAURA. SHE WON'T HAVE HEARD YOU.

Claire was hearing impaired.

WE'RE LOOKING FORWARD TO YOUR BIRTHDAY PARTY ON SATURDAY, CLAIRE!

I'M GLAD YOU'RE COMING.

HERE'S ROZ. I WANT A WORD WITH HER!

ROZ, JUST HOW LONG ARE YOU GOING TO MAKE US KEEP ON COVERING FOR YOU AND GREG?

AW, BECKY. YOU GUYS ARE BEING REALLY GOOD. JUST A WHILE LONGER, *PLEASE!*

HI, BABE. WANT A LIFT?

SURE!

BABE? OH, YUK!

16

CONTINUED ON PAGE 83.

FUNKY!

Fancy a fab 'n' funky new look? It's easy when you follow our step by step hairstyle guide. So grab a comb and a mate to lend a hand and banish those bad hair days!

STYLE 1

1. Leave two sections of hair down at the sides and put the rest up into a high ponytail at the back.
2. Start to twist the ponytail.
3. Keep twisting till it starts to coil round itself into a bun.
4. Pin the bun with hairpins and kirbies.
5. Split the two front sections into three smaller sections each and plait each small section.
6. Bring each braid back and wrap it round the bun. Secure with grips.
7. Spike up the end of the braids with a little gel or spray. Decorate the front with clips, grips or combs.

STYLE 2

1. **Put your hair into two low bunches at the back.**
2. **Back comb each bunch to make it spiky and wild.**
3. **Pin sections of the spiky bunches to the back of your head.**
4. **Fluff up any flat bits and hold in place with hairspray.**
5. **Decorate with sparkly clips or slides.**

STYLE 3

1. **Put your hair into a low, loose ponytail.**
2. **Use your fingers to split a hole above the ponytail band.**
3. Flip up the ponytail and push it through the hole.
4. **Pull it down through the hole and tighten slightly. Pin any loose bits with grips.**
5. Decorate the back with combs or slides.
6. **For extra sparkle, smooth some glitter gel through the front.**

STYLE 4

1. Put your hair into two high bunches.
2. Split each bunch into two and twist together.
3. Coil the twists round and pin securely to your head with hair pins or kirbies.
4. Spike up the ends of the coils and hold with spray or gel.
5. Decorate with hair jewels.

STYLE 5

1. Starting at the top of your head, near the back, split your hair into sections. Lifting one section at a time, spray with gel or glaze.
2. Twist each section till it goes into tight little coils.
3. Pin the little coils to your head with grips.
4. Keep going on till you have lots of coils over the top of your head.
5. Spike up the ends and decorate at the front with sparkly grips.

LONELY THIS CHRISTMAS

IT was two weeks before Christmas and Tessa James had just moved to a new house with her parents.

I LIKE OUR NEW HOUSE, BUT WHAT A TIME TO MOVE — JUST BEFORE CHRISTMAS! I WON'T KNOW ANYONE HERE AND IT'LL BE DEAD LONELY NOT HAVING ANYONE TO GO ROUND WITH.

23

And, a few days later —

THEY'RE ALL GORGEOUS, BUT I LIKE THIS LITTLE TABBY BEST.

YEAH, ME, TOO! IT LOOKS THE CHEEKIEST. YOUR MUM'LL LOVE IT!

KEEP THAT TABBY FOR US AND WE'LL FETCH IT WHEN IT'S BIG ENOUGH TO LEAVE ITS MUM. HAVE YOU JUST MOVED HERE?

YES. WE'VE ONLY BEEN HERE A WEEK.

WHY DON'T YOU COME TO OUR CHRISTMAS PARTY AT THE YOUTH CLUB ON FRIDAY? IT'S ONLY DOWN THE ROAD. YOU COULD MEET ALL OUR MATES.

THAT SOUNDS GREAT! THANKS — I'D LIKE THAT!

On Christmas morning —

I THOUGHT THIS WAS GOING TO BE A REALLY LONELY CHRISTMAS, BUT IT DIDN'T TURN OUT THAT WAY AT ALL. I'VE MADE A LOAD OF FRIENDS AT THE YOUTH CLUB, WE GOT OUR TREE AFTER ALL AND MUM AND DAD ARE LETTING ME KEEP *TWO* OF THE KITTENS!

THE END

And—

HERE WE ARE. LET'S SEE ABOUT BUYING A TREE.

XMAS TREES FOR SALE

HELLO. WE'D LIKE TO BUY A TREE PLEASE. ABOUT 6 FT WOULD DO IT.

OKAY. THIS WAY . . .

WHICH ONE WOULD YOU LIKE?

GULP!

I COULDN'T BEAR TO SEE THE LITTLE TREES BEING CUT DOWN, SO WE'VE BOUGHT A NEW ARTIFICIAL ONE AGAIN.

MERRY CHRISTMAS, GIRLS!

The End

27

Winners!

"IT'S hopeless," Lyndsey sighed. "Lee doesn't even know my name. How can I make him *notice* me?"

"I dunno, Lynz," her friend Caroline grinned. "There's no point in asking *me* for advice about boys!"

"But I won't see him for *weeks* now it's the holidays." Lyndsey sounded desperate. "I'll *die* if I don't see him sometime!"

"No, you won't!" snapped Caroline. "And you're not going to waste the holidays moping around, either. You certainly won't see him if you sit at home all the time — but you never know what might happen if we make a point of going out and about."

"I suppose you're right," said Lyndsey. "But what'll we do first?"

"How about the cinema?" Caroline suggested. "We could buy a local paper and check what's on."

And that's how they found out about the holiday competitions!

"Look," said Caroline excitedly. "One's offering ten prizes of a week's free sports instruction at the leisure centre and one's giving away a course on make-up and beauty care. What about having a go?"

"Okay," said Lyndsey. "I don't suppose we'll win, but we can at least give it a try!"

A week later Caroline rang Lyndsey.

"Guess what?" she giggled. "I've won a prize in that competition. I've got a free week of make-up and beauty care. Yuk!"

"You'll never believe this," Lyndsey almost screamed, "but I've won a prize in the *other* competition! Just imagine *me* at the sports centre for a week!"

"How about doing a swap then?" Caroline suggested. "You can be Caroline and I'll be Lyndsey for a week and we'll both get to do something we like! No one will know."

So, on Monday morning, Caroline arrived at the leisure centre to join the other prizewinners, four girls and five boys. To her amazement, the last name on the list was Lee Collingwood — the guy Lyndsey was crazy about.

"If Lyndsey'd come on this course she'd have had a whole week with Lee," Caroline thought. "But it's too late now — she'll have checked in as me on the other course. She'll be really cheesed-off when I tell her what she's missing!"

The first session was swimming for everyone and, as Caroline struggled to come to terms with the front crawl, she heard a voice.

"Want some help?" It was Lee. "You need to keep your body level and let your arms and legs do the work," he explained. "Look — like this."

Five minutes later Caroline was managing much better — and enjoying it, too. Then, as thanks, she bought Lee a Coke when they had a break.

In the afternoon the boys played rugby and the girls had badminton coaching, but they all joined up at the end of the day and Lee smiled as they left the centre.

"See you tomorrow, Lyndsey," he said with a wink. Caroline felt herself blushing as she smiled back.

That night she decided that it might not be a good idea to upset Lyndsey by telling her about Lee being on the course.

"Yeah!" Lyndsey looked puzzled. "But I . . ."

Suddenly Lee's face lit up as he caught sight of Caroline.

"There you are," he grinned. "How are you, Lyndsey?"

Caroline looked sheepish.

"I'm not really Lyndsey," she said. "I'm Caroline. It's all a bit complicated. We'd better explain."

She hardly dared to look at Lyndsey. Now her friend would know what had been going on and she would be furious with Caroline for getting friendly with Lee behind her back.

But Lyndsey wasn't mad at all. In fact, she was smiling and waving to someone who was walking along the road towards them.

"Hi, Mike!" she called. "Come and meet my mates!"

Caroline stared as the boy came and stood by Lyndsey.

"This is Mike," she said. "His mum was taking the beauty care course and he was helping out."

Caroline grinned. From the way Lyndsey was looking at Mike, he was obviously the only boy in her life now.

Caroline turned to Lee, who still looked confused.

"Sorry about this, Lee!" she said. "I'll explain everything." And all at once she knew she didn't have a problem any more. She and Lyndsey were *both* winners!

Besides, Lyndsey was dead excited about her beauty course. She insisted on trying out all the make-up techniques on Caroline and, as the two girls giggled together at the results, Caroline *knew* she'd made the right decision. Why upset Lyndsey when her friend hadn't even mentioned Lee all evening?

The week passed quickly for Caroline. And, each day, she and Lee became more and more friendly.

At first Caroline told herself she was just keeping an eye on him for Lyndsey but, eventually, she had to admit that she liked him herself and she began to feel as if she was cheating on her friend. She was sure Lee was going to ask her out soon and, although she'd *love* to go, there was no way she could. Lyndsey would never speak to her again if she did!

On Thursday the instructor told the group that there would be a photographer there next day to take photographs and interview them about the course. Caroline's heart sank. When Lyndsey saw the picture she'd want to know why her friend had kept quiet about Lee being in the group. The truth was *sure* to come out!

Caroline lay awake all night worrying about what Lyndsey would say and, in the morning, she couldn't face going on the course. Feeling sick, she phoned the centre and said she'd twisted her ankle and couldn't come. She spent the day moping around on her own, trying to stop herself thinking about Lee while she worked out how she could square things with Lyndsey.

That evening Caroline went round to Lyndsey's house, determined to tell her friend everything. As she approached, she gasped. Lee was at the door, talking to Lyndsey.

"But I came to see Lyndsey," he said. "We missed her today and I just wanted to see if she was okay. This *is* where Lyndsey lives, isn't it?"

THE END

29

All Stars!

What's your sign?
Who are you like? Who do you like?
It's all here!

ARIES
(Mar 21-Apr 20)

YOU ARE —
Popular in and out of school as you're always full of energy, enthusiasm and good ideas. You're sometimes selfish, but you try to see the good side of things. Red's your best colour.

YOU'RE LIKE —
Dancing diva, Mariah Carey, whose birthday is March 23.

BEST GIRL FRIENDS —
Pick pals born under Leo, Pisces, Sagittarius and Aquarius.

BEST BOY FRIENDS —
Go for guys born under Aries, Gemini, Leo or Libra.

TAURUS
(Apr 21-May 20)

YOU ARE —
A good friend — kind, loyal and caring, but you can also be quite stubborn. You may have a talent for singing or playing a musical instrument and like blue and pink.

YOU'RE LIKE —
Sensitive, sporty David Beckham, born on May 2.

BEST GIRL FRIENDS —
Fave friends will be born under Cancer, Sagittarius, Virgo or Libra.

BEST BOY FRIENDS —
Make mates with boys born under Gemini, Capricorn, Virgo or Libra.

GEMINI
(May 21-June 21)

YOU ARE —
Rarely quiet or still, so you could get into trouble at school, but you're also clever and good at art and drama. You can change your mind quite a lot and love the colour yellow.

YOU'RE LIKE —
Boisterous Spice Girl, Scary, whose birthday is May 29.

BEST GIRL FRIENDS —
You'll get on best with girls born under Leo, Libra, Aquarius or Gemini.

BEST BOY FRIENDS —
You'll like boys born under Aries, Gemini, Cancer or Sagittarius.

The Four Marys

IT was just before Christmas and The Four Marys, Cotter, Field, Radleigh and Simpson, friends at St Elmo's School for Girls, were heading into Elmbury to do some Christmas shopping —

PUPPIES FOR SALE

AW, LOOK AT THOSE PUPPIES!

THEY'RE SO CUTE! BUT WE'VE *THREE* DOGS AT HOME ALREADY!

LOVELY, AREN'T THEY? WHICH ONE DO YOU WANT?

I'M NOT SELLING *YOU* A PUP! *MY* DOGS ONLY GO TO *GOOD* HOMES WHERE THEY'LL BE WELL LOOKED AFTER.

MY NAME'S SMYTHE-BENNETT. I WISH TO PURCHASE ONE OF THESE PUPPIES.

IT DOESN'T REALLY MATTER. TOM WILL SOON TIRE OF IT.

31

HOW *DARE* HE INSULT ME LIKE THAT? DON'T WORRY, TOM — I'LL MAKE SURE YOU GET ONE.

I WOULD NEVER LET A DOG GO TO A BAD HOME — AND I DON'T THINK *THAT* LADY WOULD HAVE CARED FOR HER PET PROPERLY.

TOO RIGHT!

Later, in town —

YUK! THIS PERFUME'S HORRIBLE!

DAD'S BEEN LOOKING FOR THIS BOOK FOR AGES. I'LL GET IT FOR HIS CHRISTMAS.

Then snobs, Mabel and Veronica, appeared —

GOING TO HAVE A LUCKY DIP, MABEL?

GROW UP! LUCKY DIPS ARE FOR KIDS!

RUBBISH! THIS IS GREAT FUN!

BUT MABEL'S TOO STUCK UP TO ADMIT IT!

OUR PRIZES ARE REALLY GOOD!

YEAH! LET'S GRAB A COKE NEXT DOOR NOW.

So —

THAT'S ME BROKE NOW.

ME, TOO!

SAME HERE — AND I'VE STILL TO BUY CHRISTMAS CARDS!

Then —

LOOK! MABEL AND VERONICA ARE WITH THAT MRS SMYTHE-BENNETT. TRUST *THEM* TO KNOW *HER!*

. . . SO I WONDERED IF YOU'D MIND GETTING ONE FOR ME, MABEL?

NO PROBLEM, MRS SMYTHE-BENNETT. *I'LL* BUY THE PUPPY FOR YOU.

HERE'S THE MONEY — AND A LITTLE EXTRA AS A THANK YOU.

On the way back to school the Marys met the school secretary —

SUE'S PUPPY DIED — BUT I'VE TOLD HER WE'LL WAIT UNTIL AFTER CHRISTMAS BEFORE WE GET ANOTHER ONE.

BUT THAT ONE'S ALL ON HIS OWN NOW. HE'LL BE LONELY!

CHEER UP, SUE! I'M SURE SOMEONE WILL SOON GIVE HIM A GOOD HOME!

But, after The Four Marys had left —

HERE YOU ARE! HE'S ALL YOURS NOW!

THANK YOU.

YUK! IT'S TRYING TO LICK MY FACE. I'LL BE GLAD WHEN I'VE HANDED IT OVER!

Later, in The Four Marys' study —

THEY'RE NICE CARDS, COTTY.

THEY'RE NOT BAD — BUT I'LL NEED MORE.

SHH! I CAN HEAR SOMETHING!

IT'S COMING FROM MABEL'S STUDY!

LET'S HAVE A LOOK!

I THOUGHT YOU HATED DOGS, MABEL. FANCY YOU BUYING A PUPPY!

IT'S NOT FOR ME AND IT'S A PAIN! I BOUGHT IT FOR MRS SMYTHE-BENNETT.

YOU CAN'T LET THAT WOMAN HAVE THIS PUP! SHE WOULDN'T LOOK AFTER HIM! HOW MUCH DID SHE GIVE YOU TO PAY FOR HIM?

THIRTY-FIVE POUNDS!

RIGHT! WE'LL RAISE THE MONEY AND YOU CAN PAY HER BACK!

The puppy was so cute, the money was soon raised —

NOW ALL YOU HAVE TO DO IS FIND THE PUP A GOOD HOME!

WE ALREADY KNOW THE PERFECT PLACE!

And —

THIS PUPPY NEEDS A HOME, SUE. WILL YOU TAKE HIM?

OOH! THANK YOU! I'LL CALL HIM ELMO, AFTER YOUR SCHOOL!

THANK YOU, GIRLS. YOU — AND ELMO — HAVE MADE THIS A WONDERFUL CHRISTMAS!

THE END

35

WORLD WIDE!

Three puzzles in one – that's our wild world wide wordsearch. First find all the listed words hidden in the square – they can read up, down, across, backwards, forwards or diagonally. Then spot the odd one out. Finally, can you recognise the landmarks pictured on this page and say which country they come from?

```
A U S T R A L I A G R Z A Z N
O G E I R E C I X F R A N C E
M E T R U S A O B C H I X P W
A R A A K E N Y A Y J R A L Z
S A T C D N A L O P A E I T E
N N S B F E D G E M P A R Y A
R F D E N M A R K Q A T A R L
E N E G H E L E J M N N P A A
T B T Q S Y T E E E U Y X G N
S L I Z A R B C D X W E U N D
E L N B R I U E T I L M C U C
W O U S K A W S T C S Y H H Z
C H I D D S S A S O L Q A T A
A I R O M E L S V I E T N A M
T U R K E Y X R I N A I G X Q
```

AUSTRALIA
BRAZIL
CANADA
DENMARK
ECUADOR
FRANCE

GREECE
HUNGARY
ITALY
JAPAN
KENYA
LIBYA

MEXICO
NEW ZEALAND
OMAN
POLAND
QATAR
RUSSIA
SWEDEN
TURKEY
UNITED STATES
VIETNAM
WESTERN SAMOA
XUCHANG
YEMEN
ZAIRE

A

Answers on page 114.

B

C

Penny's Place

PENNY JORDAN'S parents ran Penny's Place café, the favourite meeting place of Penny and her mates —

GUESS WHAT? MY FRIEND LUCY'S COMING TO STAY FOR CHRISTMAS. SHE WAS MY BEST MATE BEFORE I MOVED HERE. HER FOLKS ARE GOING AWAY ON BUSINESS AND SHE ARRIVES TOMORROW!

COOL, PENNY! SHE'LL BE HERE WHEN WE HAVE THE BIG CHRISTMAS PARTY WE ALWAYS HOLD IN PENNY'S PLACE.

So, next day —

PENNY! HI! THIS IS MAGNUS — ISN'T HE CUTE?

SHE'S BROUGHT A DOG? I DIDN'T REALISE — IT'S NOT VERY HYGIENIC IN A CAFÉ!

SSH, MUM — IT'S TOO LATE NOW.

37

IT'S GREAT TO SEE LUCY AGAIN, AND CATCH UP ON ALL THE GOSS!

AND KATIE LEIGH'S DYED HER HAIR BLACK AND GOT A NOSE STUD!

HI, THERE!

AND GUESS WHO NATASHA'S DATING? ONLY WARREN DREW!

NO! BUT SHE COULDN'T STAND HIM!

PENNY'S SO BUSY GASSING WITH LUCY, SHE HASN'T EVEN NOTICED I'M HERE!

Just then —

DONNA GREEN! GET THAT ANIMAL OUT OF HERE!

OH, NO! SPOT'S FOLLOWED ME HERE!

COME ON, BOY — YOU'RE NOT ALLOWED IN THERE. 'COURSE, THAT LUCY'S PRECIOUS DOG IS!

Later —

HELLO, MAGNUS, WHAT HAVE YOU GOT THERE?

OH, NO! A PIECE OF STEAK! MUM'LL GO SPARE!

UPSTAIRS, MAGNUS, QUICKLY!

THERE'S SOME MEAT MISSING FROM THE KITCHEN — SOME BEST SIRLOIN STEAK!

WELL, SHE'S NOT VERY NICE!

IT'S NOT MUCH FUN DECORATING THE CAFÉ WITHOUT THE GANG. AND LUCY'S NOT INTERESTED.

OH, YOU'RE LISTENING TO BSB! AREN'T THEY THE COOLEST?

LUCY'S DRIVEN ALL MY FRIENDS AWAY. AND IT'S NEARLY TIME FOR OUR CHRISTMAS PARTY. WITH *HER* HERE, NONE OF THEM WILL BE COMING!

ONLY THE BEST IN THE WORLD!

IT'S EMILY FROM SCHOOL. I'D FORGOTTEN SHE'S AS BIG A FAN AS LUCY IS. WAIT, THIS GIVES ME AN IDEA . . .

EMILY, DON'T YOU HAVE THE VIDEO OF THEIR LAST LIVE CONCERT? I BET LUCY WOULD LIKE TO SEE IT.

WANT TO? WE CAN GO TO MY PLACE NOW.

LET'S GO!

DONNA, LUCY'S OUT OF THE WAY, SO *PLEASE* COME AND HELP ME PUT UP THE CHRISTMAS DECCIES! AND BRING THE OTHERS.

WELL — OKAY, IF YOU PROMISE SHE'S NOT THERE.

Soon —

IT'S JUST LIKE OLD TIMES WITHOUT HER.

I'M SORRY, GUYS. SHE NEVER USED TO BE SUCH A PAIN.

SHAME SHE'S GOING TO BE AROUND FOR OUR CHRISTMAS PARTY.

42

43

All Stars!

What's your sign?
Who are you like? Who do you like?
It's all here!

CANCER
(June 22-July 23)

YOU ARE —
A quiet, sensitive, sympathetic soul who can be trusted to keep friends' secrets. You like to finish what you start, but you can sometimes appear moody. Your favourite colour is purple.

YOU'RE LIKE —
Strong, silent Shane from Boyzone, born on July 3.

BEST GIRL FRIENDS —
Pick pals born under Virgo, Scorpio, Pisces or Taurus.

BEST BOY FRIENDS —
Make mates with boys born under Cancer, Capricorn, Aquarius or Taurus.

LEO
(July 24-Aug 23)

YOU ARE —
Generous, full of energy and kind-hearted, although you can also be a bit bossy if you feel you're not getting your own way. You like to look good so shopping's a hobby. Orange is your best colour.

YOU'RE LIKE —
Ginger-haired Geri, born on August 6.

BEST GIRL FRIENDS —
Fab friends are born under Aries, Gemini, Leo or Sagittarius.

BEST BOY FRIENDS —
Go for boys born under Libra, Aries, Gemini or Capricorn.

VIRGO
(Aug 24-Sept 23)

YOU ARE —
Hard-working, clever and very sure of what you do and don't like. Friends are always amazed by the bargains you manage to find. You can be a bit fussy but don't like fussy things. Navy blue's the best colour for you.

YOU'RE LIKE —
Oasis star, Liam Gallagher, born on September 21.

BEST GIRL FRIENDS —
Perfect pals include those born under Taurus, Cancer, Capricorn or Aquarius.

BEST BOY FRIENDS —
Fave friends are born under Gemini, Aquarius, Libra or Taurus.

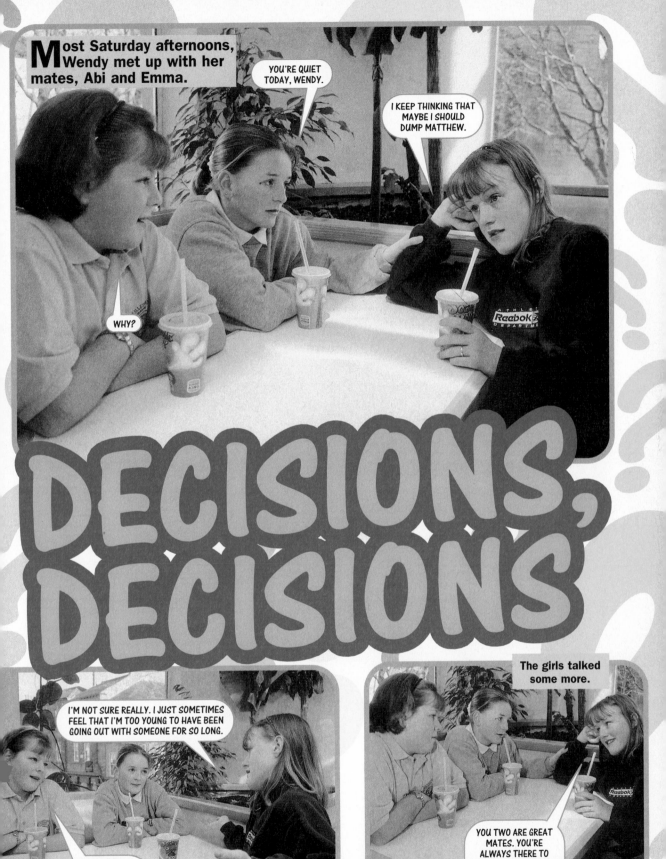

45

Next day —

HI, WENDY! DID YOU SEE MATTHEW YESTERDAY?

DID YOU DUMP HIM?

UMM — WELL, NO. I — ER — I SORT OF CHANGED MY MIND.

I JUST DON'T GET YOU, WENDY!

WELL, HE WAS DEAD NICE WHEN I SAW HIM. I MUST HAVE JUST BEEN IN A MOOD. OH, HERE HE COMES NOW.

SEE YOU LATER!

TCH! I DON'T BELIEVE HER!

SHE'S ALWAYS SAYING SHE WANTS TO FINISH WITH HIM! WE SPEND AGES LISTENING TO HER PROBLEMS, THEN SHE NEVER DOES IT!

YEAH, I KNOW. WE WERE DEAD WORRIED ABOUT HER YESTERDAY, TOO.

A few days later —

HOW ARE YOU, WENDY? WE HAVEN'T SEEN YOU FOR A FEW DAYS.

I HAVEN'T BEEN OUT. I'VE BEEN THINKING ABOUT ME AND MATT. MAYBE WE SHOULD SPLIT UP . . .

DON'T BOTHER, WE'VE HEARD IT ALL BEFORE — MANY TIMES!

THAT'S RIGHT! WE'VE SPENT HOURS LISTENING TO YOUR PROBLEMS WITH MATT. IT'S BOOO-RING!

46

Later, at home —

49

THE END

"Q" HERE TO MEET SANTA

What's going on here?

It's Santa Bug – he hasn't turned up.

MANAGER

I'll find him!

HELP!

S. CLAUS

No sign of Santa Bug. Wait – a cry for help!

I'm stuck and my reindeer are too tired to pull me out. Can you help?

I'll hitch you up to my aeroplane.

We're flying! Thanks, Bugsy!

Well done, Bugsy. You've saved Christmas.

STAR-TASTIC!

BOY BOX!

Slot the answers to these clues into our boy box and a very famous actor will appear in the shaded area.

Two pages packed with puzzles about pop, TV and film!

GIRL SWIRL!

1. Mr Smith who sings and acts.
2. A singer from Steps or 911.
3. Mr Williams.
4. An SM:tv LIVE presenter or insect.
5. Actor, Mr Pitt.
6. DJ, Mr Evans.
7. No. 4's co-presenter.
8. Backstreet Boy Mr Dorough.

The answers to all these clues are girls' first or last names ending in 'Y'. How quickly can you fit them into our girl swirl?

1. This girl sounds like a sweet.

2. Singer Mariah's surname.

Y

D'OH!

How many words of three letters or more can you make from the letters in these words?

THE SIMPSONS

SCORES
20-25 GOOD
26-35 VERY GOOD
36+ EXCELLENT

3. This Cat works with Ant and Dec.

4. She's a vampire slayer.

FIND A FRIEND!

Find the following Friends characters and actors, hidden up, down, backwards, forwards or diagonally in our fab Friends wordsearch:

JENNIFER ANISTON, MATT LE BLANC, CENTRAL PERK, COURTENEY COX, CHANDLER, FRIENDS, JOEY, LISA KUDROW, MONICA, MATTHEW PERRY, PHOEBE, RACHEL, ROSS, DAVID SCHWIMMER.

A	J	G	K	R	E	P	L	A	R	T	N	E	C	R	J
H	B	K	L	M	F	N	O	P	E	M	N	S	E	E	S
C	I	C	L	E	L	E	R	P	O	O	E	M	N	M	A
R	J	X	D	E	O	N	E	N	Q	A	T	N	I	M	R
T	O	O	U	B	H	C	I	L	N	R	I	M	H	I	E
E	M	C	E	E	U	C	O	S	S	F	E	T	E	W	W
B	A	Y	L	Y	A	L	A	T	E	S	I	W	E	H	R
M	T	E	A	N	O	W	A	R	E	T	S	H	E	C	A
C	T	N	A	L	I	S	A	K	U	D	R	O	W	S	S
L	L	E	D	S	H	N	W	H	R	Y	F	I	R	D	L
T	E	T	F	R	I	E	N	D	S	R	H	I	E	I	H
O	B	R	B	S	R	N	O	W	A	S	A	B	D	V	O
H	L	U	T	E	C	H	A	N	D	L	E	R	G	A	P
A	A	O	Y	G	L	V	E	H	S	O	L	L	S	D	I
V	N	C	H	P	S	P	A	T	H	C	L	L	E	W	N
I	C	E	R	Y	R	R	E	P	W	E	H	T	T	A	M

YIKES!

Which initials are missing from these top TV programmes?

1. The – Zone
2. – – : – – LIVE
3. – – – Friday

ALL CHANGE!

Change **STAR** into **TREK** in a few easy steps, changing just one letter at a time. We've helped you out with a few stages.

STAR
1. – – – –
2. – – – –
3. **FEAT**
4. – – – –
5. **FRET**
6. – – – –
7. – – – –
TREK

TRUE OR FALSE?

Some of these 'facts' are true, some are not. You decide!

1. Natalie Portman was discovered in a pizza parlour.
2. Chris Evans collects different colours of jelly beans.
3. The real name of Charlotte Church is Charlotte Steeple.
4. Britney hates her feet.
5. Lolly's nickname at school was 'Sweet'.

Answers on page 114.

YOU TALK TO IT, AND WHEN IT GETS USED TO YOUR VOICE IT REPEATS WHAT YOU SAY. LISTEN — HAPPY CHRISTMAS!

HAPHAPGOLAGOOK! HAPACISMOOK!

HA! HA! ALWAYS SAID YOU TALKED A LOT OF RUBBISH, SIS!

Next day Alice's friend, Cathy, came round —

HAPPY CHRISTMAS, CATHY!

SQUEAKIE'S TALKING PROPERLY NOW AND I'VE TAUGHT HIM TO SAY SOME THINGS. ISN'T HE FAB?

YEAH! YOU'RE DEAD LUCKY, AL! I WANTED ONE, BUT THEY'D ALL SOLD OUT BY THE TIME MUM GOT THERE.

ALL SAINTS ARE THE BEST!

NO, THEY'RE NOT! SAY CLEOPATRA, SQUEAKIE! CLEOPATRA!

ALL SAINTS ARE THE BEST! CLEOPATRA! CLEOPATRA!

YOUR SQUEAKIE'S GREAT, AL! I HAVE TO GO NOW, BUT I'LL COME ROUND AGAIN TOMORROW. I WANT TO HEAR WHAT ELSE IT CAN SAY!

ALL SAINTS ARE THE BEST! CLEOPATRA! CLEOPATRA!

I'D BETTER SWITCH HIM OFF NOW. HUH! CLEOPATRA! I WISH CATHY HADN'T MADE HIM SAY THAT. CLEOPATRA ARE RUBBISH!

Next day —

HELLO, SQUEAKIE! SAY 'HELLO, CATHY!'

HELLO, CATHY! HUH! CLEOPATRA! I WISH CATHY HADN'T MADE HIM SAY THAT. CLEOPATRA ARE RUBBISH!

WHAT A ROTTEN TRICK, SAYING THAT BEHIND MY BACK, AL!

BUT I *DIDN'T*! HONEST, CATHY! I *NEVER* SAID THAT TO SQUEAKIE.

YOU MUST HAVE! HE COULDN'T MAKE IT UP ON HIS OWN. WELL, I'M NOT HANGING AROUND IF YOU'RE GOING TO PLAY STUPID JOKES LIKE THAT.

WAIT A MINUTE, CATHY! YOU'VE GOT IT ALL WRONG . . .

THAT'S WEIRD. I *THOUGHT* THAT BIT ABOUT CLEOPATRA BEING RUBBISH, BUT I DIDN'T THINK I *SAID* IT. I SUPPOSE I MUST HAVE DONE, THOUGH, 'COS SQUEAKIE HEARD IT. I'LL HAVE TO BE CAREFUL NOT TO DO THAT AGAIN!

A little later —

NO PROBLEM, LISA! MAYBE ANOTHER TIME?

DARREN'S STILL TRYING TO GET A PARTNER FOR THE NEW YEAR'S EVE DISCO. AND IT SOUNDS LIKE LISA'S TURNED HIM DOWN.

Later —

GREAT! I'LL PICK YOU UP AT SEVEN ON FRIDAY, EMMA.

DARREN'S FOUND SOMEONE AT LAST! BUT EMMA'S NOT EXACTLY TOP OF HIS LIST — SHE MUST BE THE TENTH GIRL HE'S ASKED!

That evening —

HI, DARREN! I THOUGHT I'D JUST POP ROUND TO SEE IF YOU WANTED TO BORROW THIS CD.

OH! ER — HI, EMMA! COME IN!

WOW! LOOKS LIKE EMMA'S KEEN ON DARREN!

HEY — YOU'VE GOT A SQUEAKIE! DOES IT WORK?

YEAH! I'LL SHOW YOU!

DARREN'S FOUND SOMEONE AT LAST! BUT EMMA'S NOT EXACTLY TOP OF HIS LIST — SHE MUST BE THE TENTH GIRL HE'S ASKED!

OH, NO!

WHAT?

SO THAT'S WHAT YOU THINK OF ME! WELL, YOU CAN FIND SOMEONE ELSE, DARREN SCOTT!

EH? BUT I DIDN'T SAY THAT. WAIT, EMMA . . .

THANKS A BUNCH, ALICE! I'LL NEVER FIND A PARTNER NOW!

SORRY, DARREN. I DIDN'T MEAN TO SPOIL THINGS FOR YOU.

POOR DARREN! NO WONDER HE'S MAD AT ME. BUT HOW DID IT HAPPEN? I DON'T THINK I SAID THAT BIT ABOUT EMMA OUT LOUD, BUT I MUST HAVE DONE WITHOUT REALISING. I REALLY MUST BE MORE CAREFUL.

A few days later —

GRAN'S COMING ROUND TODAY, BUT DON'T SAY ANYTHING TO HER ABOUT THE PARTY ON SATURDAY.

OKAY, MUM.

I MUST BE CAREFUL. WE'RE HAVING A BIG SURPRISE PARTY FOR GRAN'S BIRTHDAY AND IT'D SPOIL EVERYTHING IF SHE FOUND OUT.

60

And, later —

IT'S SO NICE OF YOU TO ASK US OVER FOR TEA ON SATURDAY. I'VE JUST BOUGHT A FEW THINGS TO HELP OUT.

HI, GRAN!

GREAT! SHE HASN'T A CLUE ABOUT THE SURPRISE PARTY!

HELLO! WE'RE HAVING A BIG SURPRISE PARTY FOR GRAN'S BIRTHDAY AND IT'D SPOIL EVERYTHING IF SHE FOUND OUT.

A SURPRISE PARTY FOR MY BIRTHDAY? WHAT'S ALL THIS ABOUT?

OH, NO!

ALICE! HOW COULD YOU? YOU KNEW WE WANTED IT TO BE A BIG SURPRISE. NOW YOU'VE RUINED IT — YOU AND THAT STUPID TOY!

I'M — I'M SORRY, MUM.

WHAT'S GOING ON? THAT'S THE THIRD TIME SQUEAKIE'S CAUSED TROUBLE. I KNOW I DIDN'T SAY ANYTHING TO HIM ABOUT THE PARTY, SO HOW COME HE KNEW WHAT TO SAY? IT'S SPOOKY!

I DON'T WANT ANY MORE TROUBLE, SO I WON'T TALK TO HIM ANY MORE. I'LL SWITCH HIM OFF AND SHUT HIM UP IN THE CUPBOARD.

The day before the new term started —

I THOUGHT YOU WERE GOING TO TIDY UP DURING THE HOLIDAYS? YOUR ROOM'S STILL A MESS.

I KNOW. BUT I'VE GOT A PROJECT TO FINISH FOR SCHOOL.

BRILL! THAT'LL STOP MUM NAGGING. THERE'S ONLY ONE PAGE OF MY PROJECT TO COPY OUT, THEN I CAN READ MY MAG IN PEACE!

61

A few minutes later —

COFFEE! THANKS, MUM!

WHAT'S THAT NOISE? IT'S COMING FROM THE CUPBOARD.

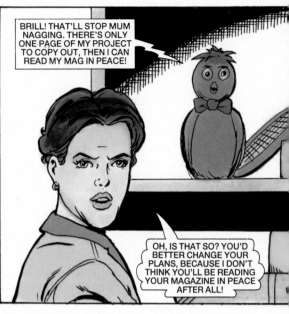

BRILL! THAT'LL STOP MUM NAGGING. THERE'S ONLY ONE PAGE OF MY PROJECT TO COPY OUT, THEN I CAN READ MY MAG IN PEACE!

OH, IS THAT SO? YOU'D BETTER CHANGE YOUR PLANS, BECAUSE I DON'T THINK YOU'LL BE READING YOUR MAGAZINE IN PEACE AFTER ALL!

THERE'S SOMETHING DEAD CREEPY ABOUT SQUEAKIE. HE SEEMS TO KNOW THINGS I'VE THOUGHT. I'D BETTER GET RID OF HIM BEFORE HE LANDS ME IN MORE TROUBLE!

Next morning —

OH — THERE'S THE SCHOOL BUS! I WAS GOING TO PUT SQUEAKIE IN THE DUSTBIN, BUT I'M TOO LATE. NOW I'LL HAVE TO TAKE HIM TO SCHOOL WITH ME.

At lunchtime —

I HAVEN'T TOLD ANYONE I'VE GOT SQUEAKIE WITH ME AND THERE HASN'T BEEN ANY TROUBLE SO FAR.

At the end of the last lesson —

BRILL! MR CHAPMAN'S FORGOTTEN TO GIVE US ANY HOMEWORK!

62

MR CHAPMAN'S FORGOTTEN TO GIVE US ANY HOMEWORK! MR CHAPMAN'S FORGOTTEN TO GIVE US ANY HOMEWORK!

WHAT WAS THAT? AH, YES! HOMEWORK!

YOU STUPID CREEP, ALICE SCOTT! WHY DID YOU HAVE TO REMIND OLD CHAPPIE ABOUT THE HOMEWORK?

ALL MY MATES ARE MAD AT ME NOW AND IT'S ALL SQUEAKIE'S FAULT. THERE'S THE SHOP WHERE MUM BOUGHT HIM. I WONDER IF THEY'D TAKE HIM BACK?

So —

AH! THIS IS THE ONE WE'VE BEEN LOOKING FOR! IT WAS SOLD BY MISTAKE — IT'S A PROTOTYPE THAT'S SENSITIVE TO THOUGHT WAVES AS WELL AS SOUND. I'LL GIVE YOU ANOTHER ONE IN EXCHANGE IF THAT'S OKAY.

GREAT — THANKS!

SO THERE *WAS* SOMETHING ODD ABOUT SQUEAKIE! HE COULD TELL WHAT I WAS *THINKING* AS WELL AS WHAT I *SAID!* NO WONDER THERE WAS TROUBLE!

Back home —

THIS SQUEAKIE SHOULD BE NORMAL, BUT I'M NOT TAKING ANY RISKS. IT'S NEVER GOING TO LEARN TO TALK. I'LL NEVER SAY ANYTHING TO IT — THEN IT CAN'T LAND ME IN TROUBLE!

When Alice had gone —

THAT'S WHAT *YOU* THINK, ALICE! I'LL MAKE YOUR LAST SQUEAKIE LOOK LIKE A PUSSYCAT!

THE END

63

Party Girls

Best friends Zara and Lynn love to party and wanted a sparkly Christmas look for going to all their discos.

ZARA is ten and lives with her mum, dad, brother and sister. She has a hamster and goldfish.

LIKES
Friends
Vengaboys, Steps and Five
Pasta, noodles and pizza
Purple
Tenerife
Singing and dancing
Skating

DISLIKES
Neighbours
Boyzone
Maths
Brussels sprouts

LYNN lives with her mum, dad and three sisters. She's ten and she has a dog, a cat and eight fish.

LIKES
Shania Twain
Maths
Cheese and tomato pizza
Scott FIVE
Shopping
Talking
Sports
Enid Blyton books

DISLIKES
Hollyoaks
Boyzone
Tomatoes
Potatoes
Language at school

ZARA → → → → →

Eyes: A pale pink eyeshadow was brushed all over Zara's eyeli right up to her eyebrows. Then bright pink glitter was added alc Zara's brow bone and shiny hearts and stars were stuck on at t outer corners. Two coats of black mascara completed the eye make-up.

Lips: Rosy pink gloss to match Zara's top finished the look.

Hair: Funky braids look great and are easy to do.

1. Leaving a section out at each side, pull your hair into a pony tail. Twist it up at the back and secure with grips.
2. Split the left-out sections into lots of little sections and plait them into small braids.
3. Coil the braids on top of your head and hold with more grips.
4. Fluff up all the ends and keep everything in place with some spray. Decorate with velcro hair jewels.
5. Brush some hair mascara and glitter through the fringe.

MAKE-UP

Face: *Keep a light, fresh look. Dot concealer over any big spots and blend in. Even out your colour and disguise any blotchy bits with tinted moisturiser in natural.*

Cheeks: *With a chunky brush, add pale shimmery pink or peach to the fattest part of your cheeks (blow your cheeks out like you're blowing up a balloon and then put your blusher on).*

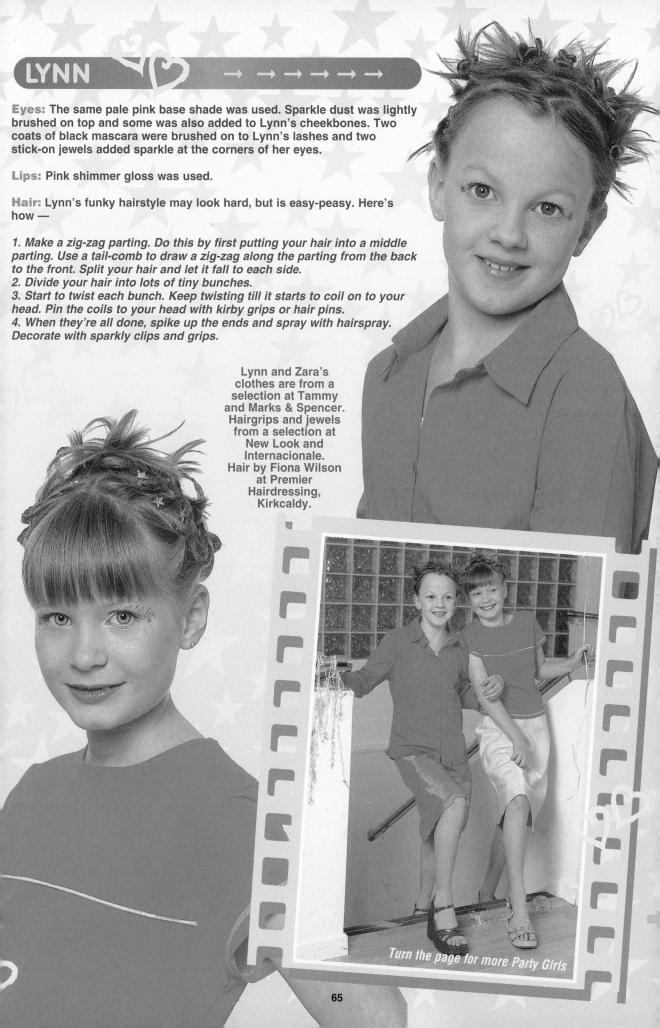

LYNN

Eyes: The same pale pink base shade was used. Sparkle dust was lightly brushed on top and some was also added to Lynn's cheekbones. Two coats of black mascara were brushed on to Lynn's lashes and two stick-on jewels added sparkle at the corners of her eyes.

Lips: Pink shimmer gloss was used.

Hair: Lynn's funky hairstyle may look hard, but is easy-peasy. Here's how —

1. Make a zig-zag parting. Do this by first putting your hair into a middle parting. Use a tail-comb to draw a zig-zag along the parting from the back to the front. Split your hair and let it fall to each side.
2. Divide your hair into lots of tiny bunches.
3. Start to twist each bunch. Keep twisting till it starts to coil on to your head. Pin the coils to your head with kirby grips or hair pins.
4. When they're all done, spike up the ends and spray with hairspray. Decorate with sparkly clips and grips.

Lynn and Zara's clothes are from a selection at Tammy and Marks & Spencer. Hairgrips and jewels from a selection at New Look and Internacionale. Hair by Fiona Wilson at Premier Hairdressing, Kirkcaldy.

Turn the page for more Party Girls

65

Sparkle!

Christmas is the perfect time to shine. You can go glittery in loadsa ways.

For all-over shine choose shimmer or glitter bath bubbles.

Go glitter crazy with roll-on body glitter, glitter sticks for cheeks, lips and body, glitter lipgloss or spray-on hair glitter. Lovely!

Add sparkle to hair with velcro hair jewels. Just press them on— easy-peasy!

Even bags or purses can add shine to your Christmas look.

Make your nails noticeable with bright metallic colours or sparkle star nail polish.

All accessories, bubble bath and glitter products from a selection at Tammy, Superdrug, New Look and Internacionale.

SPACE CADET

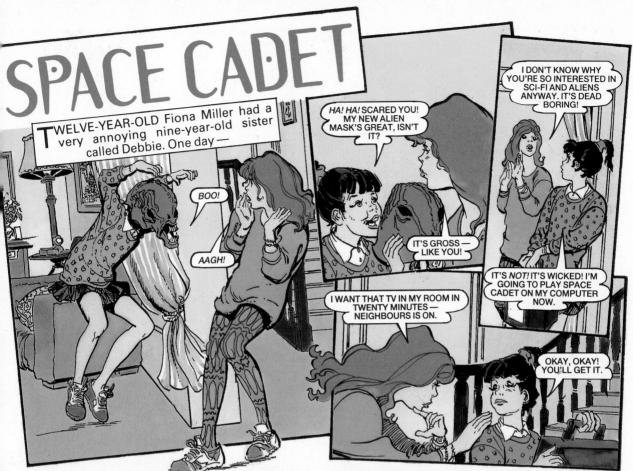

TWELVE-YEAR-OLD Fiona Miller had a very annoying nine-year-old sister called Debbie. One day —

BOO!

AAGH!

HA! HA! SCARED YOU! MY NEW ALIEN MASK'S GREAT, ISN'T IT?

IT'S GROSS — LIKE YOU!

I WANT THAT TV IN MY ROOM IN TWENTY MINUTES — NEIGHBOURS IS ON.

I DON'T KNOW WHY YOU'RE SO INTERESTED IN SCI-FI AND ALIENS ANYWAY. IT'S DEAD BORING!

IT'S NOT! IT'S WICKED! I'M GOING TO PLAY SPACE CADET ON MY COMPUTER NOW.

OKAY, OKAY! YOU'LL GET IT.

But, twenty minutes later —

I WANT THE TV NOW! TURN THAT GAME OFF!

I CAN'T, FI! I'M DOING BRILLIANTLY! I'M ON FOR A RECORD SCORE.

I KNEW THIS WOULD HAPPEN! MUM, MAKE HER TURN IT OFF!

BUT I'LL LOSE MY SCORE!

DON'T BE MEAN, FIONA. LET DEBBIE FINISH HER GAME. YOU CAN WATCH NEIGHBOURS DOWNSTAIRS.

AND HAVE TO LISTEN TO DAD'S SNIDE REMARKS — I DON'T THINK SO!

WHY DID I HAVE TO HAVE A SISTER LIKE DEBBIE? SHE'S SUCH A PAIN!

IT'S JUST A STAGE SHE'S GOING THROUGH. SHE'LL CHANGE.

I DOUBT IT!

A few days later —

IT'S QUIET IN HERE — WHERE'S DEBBIE?

IN THE TREE HOUSE — SHE'S PRETENDING IT'S HER LUNAR CONTROL MODULE.

ANYWAY, IT'S TIME FOR HER BATH. GO AND GET HER, FIONA.

SHE WON'T LIKE THAT! MY SIS HATES SOAP AND WATER.

But, just then —

I'VE COME FOR MY BATH.

EH? WHAT'S GOT INTO HER?

SEE, FIONA. I TOLD YOU SHE'D CHANGE.

MUM'S TOO TRUSTING! I KNOW DEBBIE — SHE'S UP TO SOMETHING.

Later —

OH, NO! SHE'S PLAYING THAT STUPID COMPUTER GAME AGAIN.

IT'S MY TURN TO HAVE THE TV, DEBS!

CERTAINLY. I WILL SACRIFICE MY GAME. HERE YOU ARE, FIONA.

EH? SHE'S NEVER GIVEN UP THE TV BEFORE WITHOUT A FIGHT. PERHAPS DEBBIE HAS CHANGED.

I WILL HOLD THE DOOR OPEN FOR YOU WHILE YOU CARRY THE TV OUT.

I DON'T BELIEVE IT!

A few days later —

DEBBIE'S BEEN SO GOOD RECENTLY SHE CAN KEEP THE TV TONIGHT. I'LL LISTEN TO MY STEREO.

68

69

70

READY, TeDDY, GO!

Lauren Moss, Dunstable made her own teddy bear, **Snuffles,** so he's special. We were soooo impressed that we took Lauren and Snuffles along to **The Bear Room** in Luton to meet some of the special teddies there.

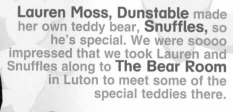

Lauren and Snuffles meet Jock the Golfing Bear. Jock is an exclusive British bear who has his own set of golf clubs and real leather golfing shoes! And just look at all the teddies behind them! Some of them are really expensive!

If you go down through the hedge today . . .

. . . you'll meet Picnic Bear with his picnic set. Picnic is a Steiff Bear (the 1997 club edition) and can only be sold to Steiff club members.

Then there's Ben. Check out the denims, girls. He's a cool British Bear Artist teddy.

Now Snuffles envies this antique Chad Valley bear's top. This bear was made in the fifties and Snuffles thinks, "He's not even threadbare."

BEAR FACTS

The first Teddy Bear was made by Margaret Steiff in 1902 and Steiff is still one of the leading bear makers in the world. They have their own club and the trade mark of a Steiff bear is the button in the ear. Limited editions are made every year and are very collectable and expensive. The bears take the name Teddy from American President, Teddy Roosevelt, who was kind to live bears.

Then we meet Boss Bear. He's a Steiff and a 1933 replica of a bear made by Steiff in 1907. Boss has leather pads and a gr-gr-growler.

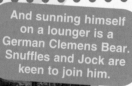

And sunning himself on a lounger is a German Clemens Bear. Snuffles and Jock are keen to join him.

And what better way to end the day than with a Teddy Bears' Picnic!

All Stars!

What's your sign?
Who are you like? Who do you like?
It's all here!

LIBRA
(Sept 24-Oct 23)

YOU ARE —
Always on the go, full of gossip and coming up with bright ideas, you're very popular. Friends might like you to quieten down a little at times, though. You're good at most things and like the colour copper.

YOU'RE LIKE —
Party girl, Shaznay All Saint, whose birthday is on October 14.

BEST GIRL FRIENDS —
Make mates with girls born under Taurus, Leo, Pisces and Aquarius.

BEST BOY FRIENDS —
You'll get on with guys born under Aries, Cancer, Gemini or Libra.

SCORPIO
(Oct 24-Nov 22)

YOU ARE —
Determined to get your own way and do things by yourself, you're always full of energy. You like sports and are good at them, always wanting to win. You like romance and love the colour crimson.

YOU'RE LIKE –
Competitive Ant McPartlin, born on November 18.

BEST GIRL FRIENDS —
Pick pals born under Cancer, Capricorn, Pisces or Scorpio.

BEST BOY FRIENDS —
Go for guys born under Aquarius, Virgo, Scorpio or Aries.

SAGITTARIUS
(Nov 23-Dec 22)

YOU ARE —
A sporty sign, who likes to know everything that's going on, you're always on the go. You have lots of really good friends who like the fact that you'll try anything new. Light blue's your best colour.

YOU'RE LIKE —
Adventurous All Saint, Nicole, whose birthday is December 7.

BEST GIRL FRIENDS —
You'll like girls born under Aries, Taurus, Leo and Sagittarius.

BEST BOY FRIENDS —
Make mates with boys born under Aries, Libra, Aquarius or Pisces.

CONTINUED FROM PAGE 17.

The Comp

PART 2

WHAT'S HAPPENED? LOOKS LIKE THERE'S BEEN AN ACCIDENT!

CLAIRE! OH, NIKKI, WHAT'S HAPPENED?

OH, ROZ — IT W-WAS TERRIBLE! A RED CAR JUST CAME SPEEDING OUT OF NOWHERE AND KNOCKED HER DOWN. THEY DIDN'T EVEN STOP!

A — A RED CAR? DID — DID YOU SEE WHO WAS DRIVING?

NO — IT ALL HAPPENED SO FAST.

IT WAS GREG! IT MUST HAVE BEEN. OH, THIS IS A NIGHTMARE!

At the hospital —

CASUALTY

DOCTOR, WILL CLAIRE BE ALL RIGHT?

WELL, THERE ARE NO BONES BROKEN, BUT SHE IS CONCUSSED. WE WILL HAVE TO WAIT TILL SHE WAKES UP TO ASSESS THE DAMAGE.

Next day, at Redvale Comp —

MY DAD SAYS THEY'RE BOUND TO FIND THE HIT AND RUN DRIVER.

PEOPLE LIKE HIM WANT LOCKING UP!

I WISH I'D GOT THE NUMBER OF THE CAR BUT IT WAS ALL SO QUICK — IT WAS A RED CAR JUST LIKE YOUR GREG'S, ROZ.

WELL, WE ALL KNOW IT WASN'T GREG, 'COS ROZ WAS WITH HIM IN HIS CAR AT THE TIME THE ACCIDENT HAPPENED.

Y-YES, THAT'S RIGHT.

WHAT CAN I SAY? I CAN'T RAT ON GREG. ANYWAY, I DON'T EVEN KNOW THAT IT *WAS* HIM. THERE MUST BE LOTS OF CARS LIKE HIS ON THE ROAD.

AND TO THINK IT'S CLAIRE'S BIRTHDAY ON SATURDAY.

AND WE WERE ALL GOING TO HER PARTY — AND NOW SHE'S JUST LYING THERE IN HOSPITAL.

OH, POOR CLAIRE . . .

ROZ, ARE YOU ALL RIGHT?

FINE, I — I'VE GOT A HEADACHE — I JUST NEED SOME FRESH AIR.

I HAD TO GET OUT OF THERE . . . OH! GREG'S CYCLED TO SCHOOL. BUT HE ALWAYS COMES BY CAR!

WHERE'S YOUR CAR THEN, GREG?

AT THE GARAGE — JUST FOR SOME MINOR REPAIRS.

REPAIRS? THEN IT *IS* TRUE. IT *WAS* GREG IN THAT ACCIDENT — IT *MUST* HAVE BEEN!

Roz ran back inside —

ROZ! WHAT'S WRONG?

I — I CAN'T BEAR IT ANY MORE! I *HAVE* TO TELL SOMEONE!

. . . SO I GOT OUT AND GREG DROVE OFF — AND HE WAS G-GOING IN THE DIRECTON OF WHERE CLAIRE WAS KNOCKED DOWN!

BUT THAT DOESN'T MEAN FOR SURE THAT IT WAS HIM.

BUT THIS DOES! I JUST HEARD HIM SAY HIS CAR IS IN THE GARAGE FOR REPAIRS!

THAT SETTLES IT. HE *IS* THE HIT AND RUN DRIVER. AND HE JUST LEFT CLAIRE LYING THERE, THE CREEP!

YOU *HAVE* TO GO TO THE POLICE, ROZ — FOR POOR CLAIRE'S SAKE.

I — I KNOW I DO, BECKY.

And so —

COME ON, ROZ. IT WON'T BE EASY BUT WE'RE ALL HERE TO SUPPORT YOU.

I — I THINK I KNOW THE HIT AND RUN DRIVER WHO KNOCKED DOWN CLAIRE CARTER.

IT'S ALL RIGHT, LOVE. SO DO WE. HE CAME FORWARD AND CONFESSED JUST HALF AN HOUR AGO.

THERE HE IS NOW. HE'S JUST BEEN CHARGED.

OH! BUT IT *ISN'T* GREG!

I FEEL TERRIBLE FOR SUSPECTING GREG, NOW, LAURA.

WE WERE PRETTY QUICK TO JUMP TO CONCLUSIONS TOO, ROZ — I GUESS IT'S 'COS WE NEVER LIKED HIM.

AND I'M SORRY I MESSED YOU GUYS ABOUT THE WAY I DID. HE *WASN'T* WORTH IT AFTER ALL.

IT'S COOL, ROZ.

Next day, after school —

THERE HE GOES — SURE DIDN'T TAKE HIM LONG TO FIND SOMEONE ELSE.

DO YOU WISH YOU TWO WERE STILL TOGETHER, ROZ?

NO WAY, HAYLEY. HE WAS CRAZY TO DRIVE LIKE THAT. ONE DAY HE *WILL* HAVE AN ACCIDENT. AND I SURE DON'T WANT TO BE THERE WHEN HE DOES.

Next morning —

GREAT NEWS! CLAIRE'S COME ROUND AND SHE'S GOING TO BE FINE! THE DOC SAYS WE CAN ALL VISIT THIS WEEKEND!

BRILLIANT!

So, on Saturday —

HOW'S IT GOING, BIRTHDAY GIRL?

FINE! THE DOC SAYS I CAN GO HOME NEXT WEEK. I'M SORRY THE PARTY'S GOING TO HAVE TO BE POSTPONED.

THINK AGAIN, YOUNG LADY! YOUR FRIENDS ALL CAME PREPARED.

HAPPY BIRTHDAY TO YOU . . .

I'M GLAD I'VE GOT FRIENDS LIKE YOU LOT!

AND *I'M* GOING TO CHOOSE MY FRIENDS MORE CAREFULLY FROM NOW ON — ESPECIALLY MY *BOYFRIENDS!*

THE END

87

BEST FRIENDS!

THAT'S brilliant news! Wait till I tell Michelle!" Emma snatched up the letter and ran next door to see her best friend. This was the day they had been waiting for, when they would hear which secondary school they were to move up to next term.

Michelle was sitting at the kitchen table when Emma danced towards her, waving the letter.

"We're going to Belshaw!" she chanted. "We're going to Belshaw! Isn't it brilliant?"

But Michelle said nothing and, when she looked up, Emma saw that she had been crying.

"I'm not going to Belshaw," she said, quietly. "I've got to go to Nettlefield High. It's miles away and I won't know anyone."

"Oh, no!" Emma gasped. "Can't — can't you get them to change their minds?"

"Mum and Dad are going to appeal," said Michelle, wiping her eyes. "But it could take ages, so I'll have to start at Nettlefield. Oh, Emma, why can *you* go to Belshaw and not me?"

"I don't know," said Emma, miserably. She didn't fancy starting at the big school on her own, either. It wouldn't be the same without Michelle.

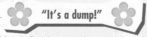

"It's a dump!"

And life at Nettlefield turned out to be as bad as Michelle had feared. Emma tried to cheer her up by saying that she was sure to make new friends soon, but that wasn't as easy as it sounded, because all the other first year pupils seemed to have friends already. After a week Michelle was *still* hanging round on her own.

What made it worse was that Emma was clearly having a great time at Belshaw. She was full of what she and her friends had been doing, what all the teachers were like and what clubs they could join. Michelle couldn't help worrying. Suppose Emma found a new best friend at Belshaw! Oh, if only she could hear about her appeal — before it was too late.

At least Michelle and Emma still met up at weekends and after school, but other girls from Belshaw had started to call in to see Emma, too, and Michelle didn't like that. Even though Emma always introduced her as her best friend, Michelle couldn't help feeling left out when the gossip was about Belshaw.

"You're at Nettlefield, aren't you?" one of the girls asked one day. "I'm glad *I* don't go there. It's a dump!"

"No, it's not!" Michelle found herself saying indignantly. "It's really good. Better than Belshaw any day."

The other girls looked at her in surprise and one or two sniggered.

"Rubbish," one of them said. "Belshaw's *much* better."

"You *would* say that," Michelle bristled. "But there's

loads going on at Nettlefield — clubs and teams and trips and things like that. It's good!" Michelle had never joined a club or been on a trip, but she was angry that the Belshaw girls were making fun of Nettlefield. Even although *she* hated it, she didn't like to hear *them* running it down.

That night, as Michelle brushed her hair, she began to make plans. If she wanted to keep Emma for herself, she'd have to break up her new gang of friends. And there was only one way to do that — make trouble!

 Secretly she was delighted.

On Monday it was Emma's birthday. Of course the Belshaw girls were at her party, and Michelle saw her chance.

First one of Emma's birthday presents, a little glass ornament, got broken. Then Emma was upset when she found someone had been in her room and tipped all her make-up out on her bed. Then the neighbours complained that the music was too loud, so Emma's mum stopped the party early.

Michelle stayed to help with the clearing-up and tried to cheer Emma up — although secretly she was delighted. No one had spotted her pushing the ornament to the edge of the table or slipping up to Emma's room. She'd even managed to turn up the music when no one was looking but, of course, Emma didn't suspect her oldest

and best friend. She suspected that it was one of the Belshaw girls who had caused the trouble.

From that day, something *always* went wrong when Michelle and the Belshaw girls visited Emma. Videos got taped over, homework went missing and drinks got spilled on the carpet. And all the time Michelle sat there looking innocent and telling them how great Nettlefield was and how many great new friends she'd made. She was *sure* her plan was working.

Then, one day, Michelle was meeting Emma at the cinema but, when she arrived, Emma was with the Belshaw gang. As she approached, Michelle could hear what they were saying.

"I don't know how you can hang round with that Michelle," said one girl. "She's a saddo."

"Yeah," said another. "Why does she have to go on about Nettlefield all the time? My cousin's there and he says she doesn't have *any* mates — and she's not in the netball team or the drama club, or anything. It's all lies, Emma."

"I — I know," said Emma. "We've been mates for years and I can tell when she's lying. But I can't just tell her to push off. Not until she *does* find some new friends at Nettlefield."

Michelle couldn't believe her ears. So Emma didn't want to be her best friend after all! Sobbing, she turned and ran home, feeling as though her whole world had collapsed round her. She never wanted to see Emma or her friends *ever* again.

When she got in, her mum was putting the telephone down.

"That was the education office on the phone," she smiled. "They've sorted things out at last, so you can start at Belshaw on Monday!"

 **THE END**

MMM... CHOCOLATE!

Rustle up some cool chocolate sweets for Christmas — or any other time of year. They're simple to make and taste totally fabsy.

● UNCOOKED FUDGE ●

Mocha

100g milk or dark chocolate.
Icing sugar.
Teaspoonful of instant coffee dissolved in a little water.

A walnut sized knob of butter.
Almonds or cherries for decoration.

Vanilla

Use white chocolate. Leave out coffee and add vanilla extract.

1. Melt the chocolate and butter in the microwave or in a bowl over a pan of water.
2. Add coffee or vanilla.
3. Mix in sieved icing sugar until the mixture is thick.
4. Press into a foil-lined baking tray and cool.
5. When firm, cut into squares or shapes and use a little icing to stick almonds or cherries on top.

● TRUFFLES ●

Choco Nut Truffles

100g milk or dark chocolate.
Walnut sized knob of butter.
Icing sugar.

Mixed chopped nuts.
Chopped dried apricots
Cocoa powder.

1. Melt chocolate and butter as before.
2. Add nuts, chopped fruit and sieved icing sugar until mixture is thick.
3. Roll into balls and toss in cocoa powder.
4. Place in mini paper cases and leave to cool.

92

CRUNCHIES

Ginger Biscuit

100g milk or dark chocolate.
3 or 4 crushed digestive biscuits.
Crystallised or glacé ginger.

1. Melt chocolate in microwave or over water.
2. Add crushed biscuit and chopped ginger until mixture is thick, but chocolate coated.
3. Place mixture in mini paper cases and cool.

Fruity Crunch

100g white chocolate.
Slightly crunched up breakfast cereal (we used Crunchy Nut flakes).
Chopped dried pineapple.

1. Melt chocolate as before.
2. Add cereal and fruit until mixture is thick but everything is chocolate coated.
3. Place in mini paper cases and cool.

Always ask an adult before using kitchen equipment.

Tropical Truffles

100g white chocolate.
Walnut sized knob of butter.
Icing sugar.
Chopped dried pineapple.
Desiccated coconut.

1. Melt chocolate and butter as before.
2. Add sieved icing sugar, chopped fruit and a spoonful of coconut. Mix until thick.
3. Form mixture into balls and roll in more coconut.
4. Leave to cool.

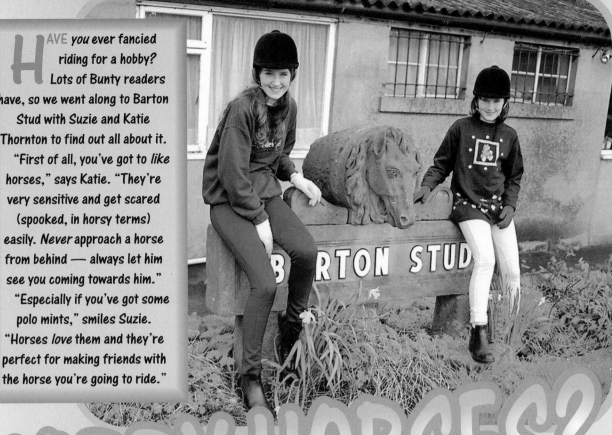

Have you ever fancied riding for a hobby? Lots of Bunty readers have, so we went along to Barton Stud with Suzie and Katie Thornton to find out all about it.

"First of all, you've got to *like* horses," says Katie. "They're very sensitive and get scared (spooked, in horsy terms) easily. *Never* approach a horse from behind — always let him see you coming towards him."

"Especially if you've got some polo mints," smiles Suzie. "Horses *love* them and they're perfect for making friends with the horse you're going to ride."

HOBBY HORSES?

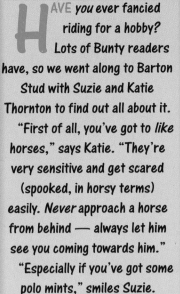

"Here's the gear we wear for riding — riding hat, sweatshirts or jackets, jodhpurs, riding boots and, in winter, gloves with fingers — not mitts. You need finger gloves to hold the reins properly."

"But you don't need all that to go along for a *first* lesson," says Katie. "Just wear sturdy shoes with smooth soles that won't get caught in the stirrups, close fitting trousers and a comfy top and you can borrow a hat from your riding school. *Never* ride without a proper hat!"

"And here's the gear the *horses* wear," laughs Suzie. "Phew! It's heavy! It's called tack."

Imagine lugging that lot about.

Suzie and Katie are "tacking up" their own ponies, Miss Molly and Omega, but this will be done for you on your first few visits to the riding school.

Tacking up means putting on the tack which consists of a numnah (blanket that goes under the saddle), girth (a strap that runs under the pony's middle to hold the saddle in place), saddle with stirrups, and the bridle, bit and reins.

All tacked up and ready to go.

On your first lesson, you'll be shown how to mount or 'get on' your horse but, first, you've to check the girth like Suzie's doing. If it's too loose, the saddle will slip about when you try to mount but, if it's too tight, the straps could pinch your horse's middle and make it play up.

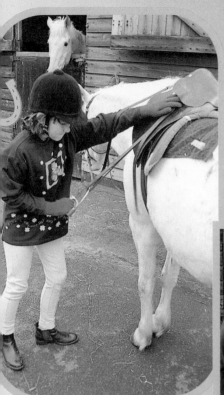

Next check that the left stirrup is at the right height for mounting then, standing on the left side of the horse, facing the tail, gather the reins loosely in your left hand and grasp a tuft of mane. Someone will hold the horse for you while you mount, which isn't as easy as it looks — at least not at first.

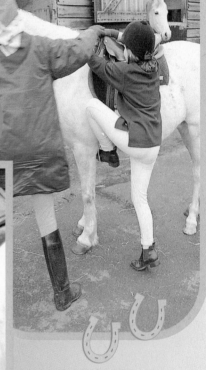

You'll also be taught how to sit properly in the saddle, keeping your head up, shoulders back and your back straight, but relaxed. Hold the reins loosely in your hands and, if you feel a bit shaky, you can grasp a bit of your horse's mane to hold on to, too. Rest your thighs and knees against the saddle and put your feet through the stirrups.

After a few lessons you'll know how to use your legs to give your horse messages and you'll be able to relax, ride and enjoy yourself — just like Suzie and Katie.

"We're off on a hack now — that's a short ride. Maybe we'll see you soon. Good luck!"

"Come on, Omega!"

"Gee up, Miss Molly!"

97

Thanks to BARTON STUD for their help.

HORSE SENSE

How much do *you* know about horses? Did you know...

- A baby horse is called a foal until it is a year old, then it is known as a yearling.
- A horse's "shoulders" are known as withers.
- Horses are measured in hands up to the top of their withers. A hand is approximately 10 cm.
- You should never feed a horse a whole carrot or apple in case it chokes. Always slice the carrot in lengths and cut an apple into pieces.
- You can roughly tell a horse's age from its teeth.
- Sugar cubes are bad for horses' teeth.
- Horses can sleep standing up as well as lying down.
- Horses' ears go back when they're frightened or angry.
- White horses are always referred to as greys.
- A horse with black and white patches is a piebald.
- Falabellas are the smallest breed of horse.
- Ragwort, bracken, deadly nightshade, acorns and yew are poisonous. A horse's field should be kept clear of them.

MIXED-UP GEAR

Unscramble the following words to make four pieces of riding gear.

SHOPDRUJ   OTOBS
TEKACJ   ATH

STEPPING OUT

A horse's walk is called its gait and a horse can travel at four paces — canter, trot, walk, gallop. Starting with the slowest, put the paces in order.

1 - - - -   2 - - - -
3 - - - - - -   4 - - - - - -

Answers on page 114.

SPOT THE DIFFERENCES

Can you find three differences between these two pictures of Suzie and Miss Molly?

SELFISH SARAH

SARAH PETERS was a very selfish girl —

SARAH, LOVE, COULD YOU GIVE ME A HAND WITH THE TEA, PLEASE?

ER — SORRY, MUM. I'VE — UM — GOT TO READ THIS BOOK FOR ENGLISH BY TOMORROW.

I DON'T REALLY, BUT MUM DOESN'T KNOW THAT!

It was the same at school.

I REALLY FANCY A BAKED POTATO TODAY, BUT I BET THEY'RE ALL GONE WHEN WE GET TO THE FRONT OF THE QUEUE!

I'LL HAVE *BOTH* OF THOSE!

OH! BUT YOU *KNEW* I FANCIED A POTATO, SARAH! HOW MEAN!

WHO NEEDS FRIENDS ANYWAY? AS LONG AS I GET WHAT *I* WANT — THAT'S ALL THAT *REALLY* MATTERS!

In class that afternoon —

DON'T FORGET YOUR GREEN ISSUE PROJECTS ARE DUE IN NEXT WEEK. THE PRIZE FOR THE BEST ENTRY IS TEN POUNDS!

RATS! I DIDN'T REALISE THERE WAS PRIZE MONEY FOR THAT STUPID PROJECT! I COULD BUY THAT TOP I LIKE WITH TEN POUNDS!

Then, on Sarah's way home —

WOW! I'VE NEVER SEEN A PLANT LIKE THIS BEFORE! I BET IT WOULD WIN ME THAT TEN POUNDS!

HELLO, DEAR. ADMIRING MY PLANT, ARE YOU?

YEAH, IT'S GREAT! ER — COULD I TAKE A SMALL CUTTING, PLEASE? IT'S FOR A SCHOOL PROJECT.

MAYBE. COME IN, DEAR, AND I'LL SOON FIND OUT IF IT'S SAFE FOR YOU TO TAKE A CUTTING.

THANKS.

EH? SAFE? I WONDER WHAT THE SILLY OLD BAT MEANS.

PUT THE KETTLE ON, DEAR, AND WE'LL HAVE A CHAT. I DON'T GET MANY VISITORS THESE DAYS.

WELL, I HAVEN'T GOT MUCH TIME. CAN I JUST TAKE THE CUTTING, PLEASE?

THERE'S NO WAY I'M STAYING HERE A MICRO-SECOND LONGER THAN NECESSARY!

I CAN'T LET YOU TAKE THE CUTTING YET. I NEED TO FIND OUT WHETHER YOU'RE SUITABLE. OH. I'M SO TIRED. WOULD YOU PUT AWAY MY SHOPPING, PLEASE?

NO WAY! I'M NOT YOUR SLAVE! LOOK — JUST GIVE ME THE CUTTING. I HAVEN'T GOT ALL DAY TO WASTE CHATTING TO *YOU*!

I'M AFRAID MY PLANT WOULD BE VERY DANGEROUS IN YOUR HANDS. YOU SEE, IT REFLECTS THE CHARACTER OF ITS OWNER, SO ONLY GOOD PEOPLE SHOULD HAVE IT.

YEAH, SURE!

SHE'S NUTS! I'M OUT OF HERE!

Soon —

HUH! THAT WOMAN JUST MADE UP A LOAD OF OLD RUBBISH BECAUSE I WOULDN'T CHAT TO HER! NOW I CAN'T WIN THE MONEY AND BUY THAT TOP!

Back home —

I CAN'T STOP THINKING OF THAT PLANT! IT WAS SO UNUSUAL! I'M POSITIVE IT WOULD WIN ME THE PRIZE MONEY!

YOU'RE VERY QUIET, LOVE. ANYTHING WRONG?

NO! BUT EVEN IF THERE WAS, I WOULDN'T TELL *YOU*!

GO TO YOUR ROOM, YOUNG LADY. I WILL *NOT* HAVE YOU TALKING TO YOUR MOTHER LIKE THAT!

HEY! I KNOW WHAT TO DO! I'LL WAIT TILL IT'S DARK, THEN GO BACK AND TAKE A CUTTING OF THAT PLANT! IT'LL SOON GROW, SO THE OLD WOMAN WON'T EVEN NOTICE IT.

101

So, later —

IF I HURRY AND GET BACK BEFORE MUM AND DAD GO TO BED, THEY WON'T EVEN KNOW I'VE BEEN OUT.

And, at the old woman's house —

GOOD, THERE'S NO-ONE ABOUT! HERE GOES — ONE LITTLE SNIP AND IT'S MINE! HA! HA!

Back home —

THIS PLANT REALLY *IS* WEIRD! THE LEAVES ARE SHAPED LIKE HEARTS AND ANIMALS. BIT SOPPY, BUT WHO CARES IF IT WINS ME THE CASH.

Next morning, Sarah checked her cutting.

I DON'T BELIEVE THIS! SOME OF THE LEAVES HAVE CHANGED! THIS ONE LOOKS LIKE A TOAD, AND THAT ONE LOOKS LIKE A WITCH'S FACE! UGH!

Later, at school —

CAN YOU GIVE ME A HAND? I'VE TRIPPED AND HURT MY LEG.

WHY SHOULD I? YOU SHOULD LOOK WHERE YOU'RE GOING!

Later, on the way home —

BRING BACK THAT CUTTING BEFORE IT'S TOO LATE! NO-ONE UNDERSTANDS THE POWER OF THAT PLANT!

I DON'T KNOW WHAT YOU'RE TALKING ABOUT! I DIDN'T TAKE ANY STUPID CUTTING!

NOT THAT SHE CAN PROVE, ANYWAY!

When Sarah reached home —

I'M GLAD YOU'RE BACK, SARAH. RUN DOWN TO THE CHEMIST AND PICK UP MRS LONG'S PRESCRIPTION, LOVE. SHE'S NOT AT ALL WELL AND I WANT TO STAY WITH HER.

OH, GREAT — NOT! NOW I'LL MISS MY FAVOURITE PROGRAMME!

I KNOW, I'LL JUST WATCH MY PROGRAMME FIRST, *THEN* I'LL GO TO THE CHEMIST. I BET MRS LONG ISN'T *THAT* ILL ANYWAY.

EH? WHAT'S GOING ON HERE? MY CUTTING COULDN'T HAVE GROWN THAT FAST — COULD IT?

When Sarah opened the door —

AHHH! HELP ME!

But the cutting had learned its behaviour from Sarah — the girl who never helped *anyone*!

THE END

103

Puzzles! Puzzles!

DO YOU KNOW?

Do you know the proper names for ① bird watching and ② bell ringing? Find the answers by using the code below.

STEPPING OUT

The answers to the following clues are all types of dancing. How many can you answer correctly?

1. You wear a tutu for this.
2. Water comes from this.
3. Up to date dancing?
4. A kilt is part of this costume.
5. Sounds like a stone moving.
6. Not English, Scottish or Welsh.

WORDSQUARE

Can you find the following hobbies in the wordsquare? Remember the words can read forwards, backwards, up, down or diagonally. Letters can be used more than once.

Swimming
Music
Karate
Dancing
Gymnastics
Brownies
Cycling
Judo
Drama
Football
Riding
Singing
Skating
Guides
Dog Walking
Skiing

O	C	D	A	N	C	I	N	G	R	E	M
D	N	O	S	D	R	O	G	J	O	T	U
U	R	G	C	R	T	U	N	P	L	A	Y
J	L	W	Y	A	G	N	I	D	I	R	N
S	L	A	C	M	G	I	G	R	H	A	G
E	A	L	L	A	N	G	N	I	I	K	S
I	B	K	I	S	I	A	I	O	L	M	C
N	T	I	N	E	T	N	S	P	J	U	Y
W	O	N	G	D	A	V	Y	T	E	S	R
O	O	G	S	I	K	H	A	N	I	I	T
R	F	O	X	U	S	F	S	T	W	C	R
B	R	N	O	G	N	I	M	M	I	W	S

Puzzles!

If doing puzzles is one of your hobbies, then get stuck into these. They're all about hobbies.

SWIMMING STROKES

Complete the missing letters to find five swimming strokes.

1. --TT--F-Y
2. B--KS--O--
3. D-G-Y -A-D--
4. C--W-
5. -R-A---T--K-

CROSS?

Cross out the letters that appear 4 times. The left-over letters will spell out another hobby.

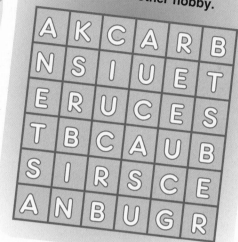

A	K	C	A	R	B
N	S	I	U	E	T
E	R	U	C	E	S
T	B	C	A	U	B
S	I	R	S	C	E
A	N	B	U	G	R

MUSICAL MATHS

Using numbers 1-5 work out the value of each instrument to answer this puzzle.

OUT OF TUNE?

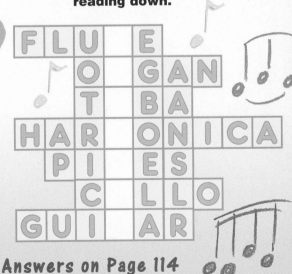

Fill in the missing letter of the musical instrument reading across to find another reading down.

F	L	U		E		
	O		G	A	N	
	T		B	A		
H	A	R		O	N	I	C	A
	P	I		E	S	
	C		L	L	O	
G	U	I		A	R	

Answers on Page 114

105

All Stars!

What's your sign?
Who are you like? Who do you like?
It's all here!

CAPRICORN
(Dec 23-Jan 20)

YOU ARE —
A nature lover who likes plants, pets and people. Sometimes grumpy, you don't *always* say what you think, but you'll always finish what you start. Your favourite colour is green.

YOU'RE LIKE —
Nice Spice Girl, Mel C, born on January 12.

BEST GIRL FRIENDS —
Perfect pals are born under Virgo, Scorpio, Taurus and Cancer.

BEST BOY FRIENDS —
Get to know boys born under Capricorn, Aries, Sagittarius or Libra.

AQUARIUS
(Jan 21-Feb 19)

YOU ARE —
A popular, kind and caring person. You're always asking questions and can get on with the grumpiest of people. You can be a little forgetful sometimes, though. Turquoise is the colour to choose.

YOU'RE LIKE —
Non-stop popster, Robbie, whose birthday is February 13.

BEST GIRL FRIENDS —
You'll make mates with girls born under Virgo, Libra, Aquarius or Gemini.

BEST BOY FRIENDS —
You'll like boys born under Cancer, Leo, Sagittarius or Scorpio.

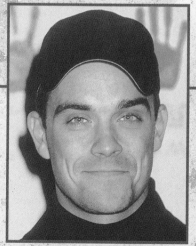

PISCES
(Feb 20-Mar 20)

YOU ARE —
Indecisive and a bit moody, but you have lots of friends because you're also kind, gentle and caring. You don't mind others making decisions for you and love greens and blues.

YOU'RE LIKE –
Romantic Ronan, born on March 3.

BEST GIRL FRIENDS —
You'll like girls born under Taurus, Gemini, Virgo or Scorpio.

BEST BOY FRIENDS —
Go for guys born under Aries, Cancer, Libra or Pisces.

The Four Marys

THE FOUR MARYS, Cotter, Field, Radleigh and Simpson, were friends at St Elmo's School for Girls. Another girl, Josie Smith, had just asked for their help —

CHANGING ROOM

SOMEONE SAW MABEL AND VERONICA SNEAKING INTO MY STUDY WHILE THEY THOUGHT I WAS OUT PLAYING SPORTS. WILL YOU LOT COME WITH ME TO SEE WHAT THEY'RE UP TO?

SURE, JOSIE!

Snobs, Mabel Lentham and Veronica Laverly, weren't popular —

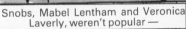

THERE! I TOLD YOU I'D SEEN JOSIE SMITH HIDING SOMETHING UNDER HERE, VERONICA!

LOOKS LIKE A FOOD HAMPER FROM HOME. WELL, WE'LL TEACH HER TO KEEP ALL HER FOOD TO HERSELF!

But —

A HEDGEHOG! YUK!

NOT WHAT YOU EXPECTED, EH?

THIS IS HORACE. HE WAS HIT BY A CAR OUTSIDE SCHOOL, SO I'M NURSING HIM BACK TO HEALTH.

IT'S DISGUSTING! WHAT ABOUT THE FLEAS?

THEY WON'T GO ANYWHERE NEAR YOU, VERONICA. FLEAS ARE CHOOSY!

A couple of days later —

JOSIE! I'VE FOUND JUST THE PLACE FOR YOUR ANIMAL HOSPITAL! IT'S REALLY COSY DOWN IN THE BASEMENT BESIDE THE CENTRAL HEATING BOILER. COME AND SEE!

And —

I'VE SPOKEN TO THE JANITOR AND HE SAYS IF YOU CLEAR OUT ALL THE JUNK AND MRS MITCHELL AGREES, YOU CAN USE THE PLACE.

IT'S *PERFECT* FOR MY ANIMAL HOSPITAL! I COULD BUILD LITTLE CAGES AROUND THE WALLS.

The Marys offered to help —

WHAT ARE THE MARYS UP TO, VERONICA?

I DON'T KNOW, BUT I'VE SEEN THEM GOING INTO THE BASEMENT. LET'S GO AND TAKE A LOOK.

And —

WOW! THIS WOULD MAKE A GREAT DEN FOR US, MABEL! WE COULD PLAY OUR CDS AS LOUD AS WE LIKED HERE AND NO-ONE WOULD HEAR THEM!

YEAH! A BIT OF CARPET AND SOME CHAIRS WOULD MAKE IT REALLY COMFY!

Just then —

ANIMAL HOSPITAL

SORRY TO DISAPPOINT YOU, BUT MRS MITCHELL SAYS *JOSIE'S* IN CHARGE DOWN HERE FROM NOW ON.

YEAH — YOU CAN STAY AND HELP IF YOU LIKE!

HUH! *THAT'LL* BE RIGHT!

109

The girls worked hard and, a few days later —

THANKS TO ALL YOUR HELP, THE ST ELMO'S ANIMAL AND BIRD HOSPITAL IS NOW WELL AND TRULY OPEN!

GREAT! WE'LL BE ASSISTANT NURSES, TOO, JOSIE. JUST TELL US WHAT NEEDS DONE.

Their nursing duties were sometimes quite unusual —

I NEVER THOUGHT WE'D BE CRAWLING ABOUT LOOKING FOR FOOD FOR BABY BIRDS, RADDY!

Then —

AS I TOLD YOU BY PHONE, I RECEIVED AN ANONYMOUS LETTER, MRS MITCHELL, ALLEGING THAT ANIMALS ARE BEING KEPT IN FILTHY CONDITIONS IN THE SCHOOL BASEMENT.

THESE ALLEGATIONS ARE UNFOUNDED. THE ANIMALS ARE WELL LOOKED AFTER. WE'LL INSPECT THE BASEMENT AFTER COFFEE.

IT'S COLONEL MASON — ONE OF THE SCHOOL GOVERNORS.

And —

IT WORKED, MABEL! OUR LETTER GOT A SCHOOL GOVERNOR HERE.

NOW ALL WE HAVE TO DO IS MAKE SURE HE FINDS THAT ANIMAL HOSPITAL TO BE A HEALTH HAZARD. ONCE THE ANIMALS ARE TURFED OUT, WE CAN TAKE OVER THE ROOM!

THEY'RE MAKING FOR THE HOSPITAL. WE'D BETTER FOLLOW THEM.

A few minutes later —

QUICKLY, BEFORE THE GOVERNOR GETS HERE WITH MRS MITCHELL! TIP THE BOWLS OVER!

YEAH — AND THIS STRAW BEDDING WILL LOOK LIKE A REAL FIRE HAZARD!

I'LL LET THESE MICE OUT AND THEN . . .

MABEL! LEAVE THOSE CAGES!

I DIDN'T THINK EVEN *YOU* TWO WOULD SINK TO THIS! GET IT CLEARED UP — *NOW!*

IT — IT WAS JUST A JOKE. PLEASE DON'T TELL MRS MITCHELL!

A little later —

SO THIS IS THE ANIMAL HOSPITAL? IT SEEMS IN ORDER TO ME — NOT AT ALL WHAT THAT ANONYMOUS LETTER LED ME TO EXPECT.

Then Mrs Mitchell saw Mabel and Veronica —

I DIDN'T REALISE YOU TWO WERE INTERESTED IN HELPING INJURED BIRDS AND ANIMALS.

ER . . . YES, MRS MITCHELL.

THIS IDEA HAS HAD EVERYONE INVOLVED, MRS MITCHELL.

WHAT A WONDERFUL PROJECT! I'M SURE A CONTRIBUTION FROM SCHOOL FUNDS COULD BE ARRANGED TO HELP RUN YOUR HOSPITAL.

THAT'S *GOOD* NEWS FOR THE SICK ANIMALS, JOSIE — BUT IT'S MADE VERONICA AND MABEL FEEL A BIT SICK, TOO! HA! HA!

THE END

111

PARTY

OR PARTY

1. When it's time to let off party poppers, where are you?
a) Lying in wait to surprise people. Ho, ho!
b) Cowering in a corner. You don't like loud noises.
c) Covered in streamers, laughing.

2. You've been invited to an ace party. What will you wear?
a) You've saved up specially for something brand new.
b) The same outfit you wore to last year's party.
c) A fave top with a glittery accessory.

3. What would invites to *your* party be like?
a) Funny, friendly and festive.
b) Glittery and sparkly — just like you!
c) Party? *What* party? You *never* have parties.

4. You're up and dancing, but to what kind of music?
a) All the Christmas classics.
b) *Dancing*? Er, you're really just shuffling backwards and forwards.
c) You're doing the latest dance to the latest hit.

5. How would *your* party be decorated?
a) With quiet Christmas decorations you've had for years.
b) In this year's cool crimbo colours with fab fluffy baubles.
c) It'd be stuffed with Santas, balloons and streamers.

6. With how many friends will you go to a party?
a) The more the merrier!
b) One — your best friend.
c) Quite a few so you can dance together.

112

POPPER
POOPER?

animal . . . or – er – not.

8. What party food will you be eating?
a) Pizza, chilli, potato skins, chips.
b) Very swanky snacks like sushi and seaweed.
c) Sandwiches, crisps, peanuts, sausage rolls.

7. There's a boy you like at the party. Where are you?
a) Gazing longingly at him from afar.
b) Asking him and his pal for a dance with you and your mate.
c) Giving chase with a big bit of mistletoe!

CONCLUSIONS

8-13

Oh, dear. You're not really into parties at all. You find them a bit loud and scary and never know what to do or wear. But it's okay to be different.

14-20

For you, parties are fun. You and your mates dress up, dance and have a bit of a laugh. You don't take them seriously at all. Enjoy your Christmas.

21+

Yikes! You're a scary party animal, all right! Never off the dance floor, first with all the latest trends, you just love a good party. So, party on!

SCORES

1. a.3 b.1 c.2
2. a.3 b.1 c.2
3. a.2 b.3 c.1
4. a.2 b.1 c.3
5. a.1 b.3 c.2
6. a.3 b.1 c.2
7. a.1 b.2 c.3
8. a.2 b.3 c.1

ANSWERS

Here are the answers to all the puzzles in this brill book. How well did you do?

STAR-TASTIC!

P.54

```
A J G K R E P L A R T N E C R J
H B K L M F N O P E M N S E E S
C I C L E L E R P O O E M N M A
R J X D E O N E N Q A T N I M R
T O O U B H C I L N R I M H I E
E M C E E U C O S S F E T E W W
B A Y L Y A L A T E S I W E H R
M T E A N O W A R E T S H E C A
C T N A L I S A K U D R O W S S
L L E D S H N W H R Y F I R D L
T E T F R I E N D S R H I E I H
O B R B S R N O W A S A B D V O
H L U T E C H A N D L E R G A P
A A O Y G L V E H S O L L S D I
V N C H P S P A T H C L L E W N
I C E R Y R R E P W E H T T A M
```

GIRL SWIRL!

1. Lolly, 2. Carey,
3. Deely, 4. Buffy

BOY BOX!

1. Will, 2. Lee, 3.
Robbie, 4. Ant, 5.
Brad, 6. Chris, 7.
Dec, 8. Howie.
The famous
actor is
Leonardo.

ALL CHANGE!

STAR, SEAR, FEAR,
FEAT, FEET, FRET,
FREE, TREE, TREK

TRUE OR FALSE?

1. True, 2. False,
3. False, 4. True,
5. False

YIKES!

1. The O Zone, 2.
SM:tv LIVE, 3. TFI
Friday

WORLD WIDE!

P.36

```
A U S T R A L I A G R Z A Z N
O G E I R E C I X F R A N C E
M E T R U S A O B C H I X P W
A R A A K E N Y A Y J R A L Z
S A T C D N A L O P A E I T E
N N S B F E D G E M P A R Y A
R F D E N M A R K Q A T A R L
E N E G H E L E J M N N P A A
T B T Q S Y T E E E U Y X G N
S L I Z A R B C D X W E U N D
E L N B R I U E T I L M C U C
W O U S K A W S T C S Y H H Z
C H I D D S S A S O L Q A T A
A I R O M E L S V I E T N A M
T U R K E Y X R I N A I G X Q
```

ODD ONE OUT

Xuchang. This *isn't* a country

A — Eiffel Tower, France

B — The Little Mermaid,
     Denmark

C— The Statue of Liberty,
     United States of America

HORSE SENSE

P.98

SPOT THE DIFFERENCES
MIXED-UP GEAR

1. Jodhpurs, 2. Boots, 3. Jacket, 4. Hat

STEPPING OUT

1. Walk, 2. Trot, 3. Canter, 4. Gallop

PUZZLES! PUZZLES! PUZZLES!

P.104

OUT OF TUNE?
Trumpet

CROSS?
Knitting

MUSICAL MATHS

DO YOU KNOW?

1. Ornithology, 2. Campanology

SWIMMING STROKES

1. Butterfly, 2. Backstroke, 3. Doggy
Paddle, 4. Crawl, 5. Breaststroke

STEPPING OUT?

1. Ballet, 2. Tap, 3. Modern, 4. Highland,
5. Rock 'n' Roll, 6. Irish

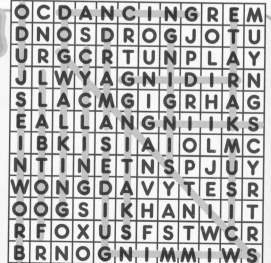

```
O C D A N C I N G R E M
D N O S D R O G J O T U
U R G C R T U N P L A Y
J L W Y A G N I D I R N
S L A C M G I G R H A G
E A L L A N G N I I K S
I B K I S I A I O L M C
N T I N E T N S P J U Y
W O N G D A V Y T E S R
O O G S I K H A N I I T
R F O X U S F S T W C R
B R N O G N I M M I W S
```

Just then the telephone rang —

THAT WAS YOUR GRAN, JADE. THEY'RE DEFINITELY NOT COMING. THE WEATHER'S TOO BAD.

RATS! THAT'S SPOILED *EVERYTHING*!

TCH! AND I THOUGHT IT WAS GOING TO BE A GOOD CHRISTMAS! OH — WHAT'S THAT NOISE? IT SOUNDS LIKE A DOG BARKING.

And —

HELLO! WHAT'S THE MATTER WITH YOU? DO YOU WANT TO COME IN?

HE SEEMS UPSET. MAYBE HE'S LOST OR SOMETHING.

WHAT'S GOING ON, JADE?

IT'S THAT DOG. LOOK AT HIM, DAD! I THINK HE WANTS US TO FOLLOW HIM.

THERE MUST BE SOMETHING WRONG. I'LL GET A TORCH AND GO AND SEE WHAT'S GOING ON.

I'LL COME WITH YOU, DAD!

Jade and her dad struggled through the snow. Suddenly —

LOOK, DAD! THERE'S A CAR STUCK IN THAT SNOWDRIFT.

THERE'S NO-ONE HERE. THE PEOPLE MUST HAVE TRIED TO WALK THROUGH THE SNOW. THEY'LL NEVER FIND THEIR WAY IN THIS BLIZZARD.

MAYBE THE DOG KNOWS WHERE THEY ARE — HE'S RUNNING OFF AGAIN.

And, eventually —

HELLO, THERE!

OH, I'M SO GLAD YOU'VE FOUND US! WE'VE NO IDEA WHERE WE ARE.

YOU MUST BE FREEZING! YOU'D BETTER COME BACK WITH US AND GET WARMED UP.

WE'VE BEEN WANDERING ROUND FOR AGES. HOW DID YOU FIND US?

IT WAS YOUR DOG. HE CAME TO OUR HOUSE AND BARKED UNTIL WE FOLLOWED HIM.

DOG? BUT WE HAVEN'T GOT A DOG.

EH? BUT THEY MUST HAVE SEEN — OH! HE'S GONE. WELL, IF HE'S NOT THEIRS, HE MUST'VE COME FROM ONE OF THE FARMS.

Back at the cottage —

I'M KEN, THIS IS SHEILA AND THAT'S KATY AND DUNCAN. I DON'T KNOW HOW TO THANK YOU FOR RESCUING US!

YOU'LL HAVE TO STAY HERE TONIGHT. THE ROADS ARE WAY TOO BAD TO GO ANY FURTHER.

117

Then —

OH, KATY, YOU'RE CRYING. WHAT'S WRONG?

S-SANTA WON'T KNOW WHERE TO LEAVE OUR PRESENTS. WE SHOULD BE AT OUR GRAN'S. HE'LL NEVER FIND US HERE!

DON'T WORRY, KATY! SANTA KNOWS *EVERYTHING*, HE'LL KNOW WHERE TO COME. HE'LL BE BRINGING *MY* PRESENTS, SO WE'LL LEAVE A NOTE TO TELL HIM *YOU'RE* HERE, TOO.

OH, YES! IT'LL BE ALL RIGHT THEN. WE *WILL* GET OUR PRESENTS!

Later —

HMM. MAYBE CHRISTMAS WON'T BE SO BAD AFTER ALL. KATY AND DUNCAN ARE HAVING FUN.

'NIGHT, JADE! IT'S REALLY EXCITING BEING HERE!

'NIGHT, KATY! 'NIGHT, DUNCAN! SLEEP TIGHT!

DAD AND KEN HAVE GONE BACK TO KEN'S CAR TO GET ALL THE PRESENTS OUT OF IT. SANTA *IS* COMING HERE.

IT WAS DEAD LUCKY THAT THAT DOG CAME FOR US. IF NO-ONE HAD FOUND KEN, SHEILA AND THE KIDS THEY'D HAVE BEEN FROZEN, WANDERING ABOUT OUT THERE ALL NIGHT.

Next morning —

JADE, LOOK WHAT I'VE GOT! IT'S THE DOLL I WANTED!

AND I'VE GOT A CAR. COOL!

MERRY CHRISTMAS, YOU TWO.

118

Later —

HMM. I WONDER WHERE THAT DOG CAME FROM? I HOPE I SEE IT AGAIN. I'LL ASK ROUND AT THE FARMS — SOMEONE'S SURE TO KNOW WHO IT BELONGS TO.

THIS IS LOVELY. YOU'VE ALL BEEN SO KIND. I CAN'T THANK YOU ENOUGH.

NO PROBLEM! IT'S BRIGHTENED UP OUR CHRISTMAS HAVING YOU HERE! MAYBE WE'LL GET YOUR CAR MOVING LATER TODAY. THE ROADS ARE A LOT CLEARER NOW.

After dinner one of the farmers came to help —

YEAH, THAT'S IT. IT'S MOVING.

Soon afterwards —

GOODBYE! AND THANK YOU! WE WON'T FORGET THIS CHRISTMAS.

'BYE, KATY! 'BYE, DUNCAN! HAVE A GOOD JOURNEY!

THEY WERE LUCKY! THEY'D HAVE BEEN IN REAL TROUBLE IN THAT BLIZZARD IF NO-ONE HAD FOUND THEM.

A BLACK AND WHITE COLLIE CAME TO THE COTTAGE AND BARKED TILL WE FOLLOWED HIM. HE TOOK US RIGHT TO THEM. DO YOU KNOW WHERE HE LIVES? I'D LOVE TO SEE HIM AGAIN.

THERE'S A BLACK AND WHITE COLLIE AT EVERY FARM ROUND HERE, LASS! IT COULD HAVE COME FROM ANY OF THEM.

HEY, DAD. MAYBE IT WAS BRUCE FROM HIGH TOP FARM. ISN'T HE SUPPOSED TO TURN UP WHEN FOLK ARE IN TROUBLE?

TCH! THAT'S JUST A LOCAL TALE. BRUCE DIED YEARS AGO SAVING HIS MASTER FROM A BURNING BARN, LASS. NOW FOLK SAY THEY'VE SEEN HIM AROUND WHENEVER THERE'S TROUBLE. BUT I'VE NEVER SEEN HIM!

A GHOST DOG? IT CAN'T HAVE BEEN! THE DOG WHO CAME TO THE COTTAGE LOOKED REAL. NO, IT MUST HAVE BEEN A COLLIE FROM ONE OF THE FARMS.

HEY! THAT'S THE DOG THERE. I'M SURE IT IS!

I'LL GO UP TO HIM. MAYBE THERE'LL BE A NAME ON HIS COLLAR. THEN WE CAN FIND THE OWNER AND TELL HIM WHAT THE DOG DID.

OH, NO! HE'S GONE! THAT'S WEIRD, THOUGH . . .

. . . THE DOG WAS HERE — I SAW IT! SO THERE SHOULD BE MARKS IN THE SNOW WHERE IT WAS STANDING, BUT THERE'S NOTHING. H-HAVE I SEEN A GHOST . . . ?

THE END

120

FOUL PLAY!
Julie had some exciting news for her friend, Clare —
HEY, CLARE, YOU'LL NEVER GUESS WHAT'S JUST HAPPENED!
DON'T TELL ME — SIMON'S ASKED YOU OUT AT LAST.
YEAH, HE HAS. I CAN'T WAIT. I'LL GIVE YOU ALL THE JUICY DETAILS ON MONDAY.
WELL, IT'S NOT BEFORE TIME. I JUST HOPE IT'S NOT A BIG LET DOWN.
On Saturday —
NOW SHOWING
HI! SORRY I'M A BIT LATE, ONLY, THE BUS GOT STUCK IN TRAFFIC.
THAT'S OKAY. YOU'RE WORTH WAITING FOR, JULIE.
MMM. SIMON SEEMS REALLY KEEN.
FANCY GOING FOR A PIZZA AFTER THE FILM? YOU DON'T HAVE TO GO RIGHT HOME, DO YOU?
NOW SHOWING
THAT'D BE BRILLIANT, SIMON.

And —

So —

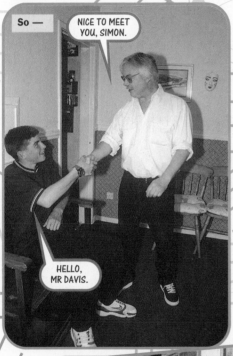

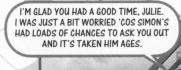

And —

I'M GLAD YOU HAD A GOOD TIME, JULIE. I WAS JUST A BIT WORRIED 'COS SIMON'S HAD LOADS OF CHANCES TO ASK YOU OUT AND IT'S TAKEN HIM AGES.

I SUPPOSE IT IS A BIT FUNNY. HE DIDN'T SHOW AN INTEREST IN ME AT DAVE'S PARTY. STILL, WHAT MATTERS IS THAT WE'RE GOING OUT TOGETHER NOW!

On Friday —

HELLO, LOVE. DID YOU HAVE A GOOD TIME WITH SIMON?

YES, THANKS, DAD. THE DISCO WAS GREAT.

I HOPE HE HASN'T FORGOTTEN ABOUT THE FOOTBALL TRIAL TOMORROW.

NO CHANCE! HE'S DEAD KEEN. I'D COME ALONG AND WATCH, BUT I DON'T WANT TO PUT HIM OFF.

STILL, WITH ANY LUCK I'LL BE BUYING HIM A PIZZA LATER TO CELEBRATE.

Next day —

SIMON SHOULD'VE BEEN HERE BY NOW. I HOPE DAD'S PUTTING HIM IN THE TEAM.

Then —

SIMON! HOW DID YOU GET ON? IS EVERYTHING OKAY?

NOT REALLY. YOUR OLD MAN TURNED ME DOWN. HE SAID ONE OF THE OTHER LADS WAS BETTER THAN ME.

On Monday —

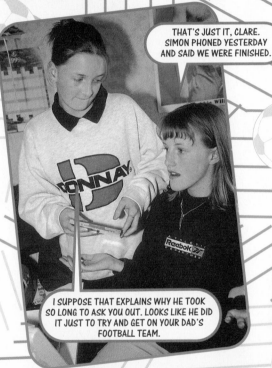

THE END

125

Play this game with your friends to see who's a winter winner!

Winter

MOVE ON

(5) ● Pull on speed skates. Zoom on 4.

(11) ● Avoid being hit by snowballs. Stomp on 2.

(22) ● Slip forward 3 spaces on ice.

(29) ● A friend pulls you along 2 spaces.

(53) ● Your outfit's ultra-trendy. Move on 3.

(61) ● You're neck and neck with a pal. Move on 1.

(64) ● You sledge past everyone 4 super spaces.

GO BACK

(14) ● A ski snaps. Yikes! Go back 5.

(24) ● Your goggles ping off. Go back 4.

(28) ● You veer off in the wrong direction. Go back 2.

(38) ● You hit a block of ice and bounce back 5.

(43) ● Your ice skate laces snap. Go back 3.

(51) ● Gaze at hunky ski instructor. Go back 1.

(60) ● You slip and end up back to front. Go back 3.

(67) ● Your hat blows off. Go back 2.

START →

126